THE PETROLEUM INDUST

OF THE SOVIET UNION

By Ro

S

THE PETROLEUM INDUSTRY

OF THE SOVIET UNION

ROBERT E. EBEL

THE PETROLEUM INDUSTRY
of the
SOVIET UNION

Produced by ROYER & ROGER, Inc.

FOREWORD

In August of 1960 a team of oil experts, selected and sponsored by the American Petroleum Institute at the request of the Department of State, toured a number of oil fields, refineries and petroleum research institutes of the Soviet Union. This visit took place under the US-USSR Exchange Agreement of November 21, 1959, which provides for exchanges in scientific, technical, educational and cultural fields. The Exchange Agreement was entered into in the hope that such exchanges will contribute significantly to the betterment of relations between the two countries, thereby contributing to a lessening of international tension.

In reciprocity for the visit of the US delegation to the USSR, a group of Soviet experts arrived in this country in early October, 1960, to spend 30 days touring selected oil facilities in widely separated parts of the country.

It is believed that the exchange of oil delegations between the US and the USSR fulfilled the purpose set forth in the Exchange Agreement of contributing to the betterment of relations between our two countries. It is also believed that further reciprocal visits in this area would be useful to both countries and could provide both information and personal understanding of lasting benefit.

W. W. KEELER
Executive Vice President,
Phillips Petroleum Company,
and Chairman of the US Oil Delegation

i

DEDICATION

This book is respectfully dedicated to the memory of Whitney K. Elias, a member of the first US oil delegation to the USSR in 1960, who died in Paris shortly after completion of the tour of the delegation.

"Whit" Elias was an avid and highly motivated student of the petroleum industry who was inspired by an intense sense of responsibility and guided by an insatiable curiosity. His observations during the stay of the delegation in the Soviet Union, particularly in production matters, made a significant contribution to this publication.

FRANK M. PORTER
President
American Petroleum Institute

ACKNOWLEDGMENT

This report amplifies a preliminary report of the US oil delegation to the USSR — US Oil Men Take a Look at Russia — which was submitted to the American Petroleum Institute in November, 1960. It represents an attempt to present in more comprehensive form a current analysis of the Soviet oil industry together with probable future courses of development.

The study has as its basis the written notes and observations of the members of the US oil delegation. Because the scope of the exchange was limited to production, research and refining, a thorough investigation of the Soviet petroleum industry, drawing solely on these observations, would not be possible. To accomplish this, the writer has turned to the vast amount of information available to the Western observer in the many technical books, magazines and daily newspapers published in the Soviet Union.

Recognition is due to the other members of the delegation for their careful and expert analysis of the Soviet petroleum industry which has provided the gauge of objectivity necessary to this report, and for their effective criticism of its contents. The chapter on Research Impressions is largely the work of Neal J. Smith, who also collated the notes on those oil fields visited by the delegation. W.W. Keeler, in coordination with George T. Piercy and George Dunham, is responsible for the notes on refineries visited by the delegation. The American Petroleum Institute and especially its Washington representative, Frank Dennis, have offered every assistance to the writer in the preparation of the manuscript.

The author particularly wishes to express his appreciation to Alexander Gakner, Assistant Vice President of Royer and Roger, Inc., whose personal interest in this book and supervision of its production have been most valuable. Alexander Gakner, a member of the US oil delegation, was formerly with the Bureau of Mines, US Department of the Interior.

Personal articles by members of the delegation embracing the visit of the US oil delegation to the USSR have appeared in Petroleum Today, GeoTimes, The Lamp, and The Saturday Evening Post.

R.E.E.

Arlington, Virginia
June 1961

TABLE OF CONVERSIONS

	Multiplied by	Equals
Meters	3.281	feet
Kilometers	0.621	miles
Cubic meters	35.314	cubic feet
Metric tons	7.3	barrels
	0.02	barrels per day
Barrels per day	50	metric tons per year
Hectares	2.471	acres
Square kilometers	0.386	square miles
Metric ton	1.102	short ton (2,000 lb)
Square meters	10.764	square feet

A metric ton of standard fuel has a calorific value of 7,000 kilocalories per kilogram, or the equivalent of 27,780,000 British thermal units per metric ton. To convert the following types of fuel into metric tons of standard fuel, apply these factors:

Coal: 0.750 metric tons of standard fuel per metric ton.
Crude oil: 1.43 metric tons of standard fuel per metric ton.
Natural gas: 1.2 metric tons of standard fuel per 1,000 cubic meters.
Peat: 0.379 metric tons of standard fuel per metric ton.
Shale: 0.343 metric tons of standard fuel per metric ton.
Hydroelectric power: 0.463 metric tons of standard fuel per 1,000 kilowatt hours.

The conversion factor for crude oil is constant, but those for the other fuels are applicable only in 1960, as heat values and therefore conversion factors vary yearly as a reflection of the production mix and/or of production quality.

Prior to 1 January 1961, the official exchange rate set the value of the ruble at 25¢. The tourist exchange rate provided 10 rubles for each $US1, or 10¢ for each ruble. The ruble reform, which took place at the beginning of 1961, represented a devaluation of that currency. The new ruble, equal to 10 old rubles, has been declared to be worth $US1.11.

All of the ruble quotations in this report are in old rubles. In addition, all conversions of rubles to $US have been made at the then existing official exchange rate of 4 to 1. While it is recognized that this value placed on the ruble is exaggerated, the degree of exaggeration is not known, therefore use of the official exchange rate has been necessary.

CONTENTS

I. GENERAL INFORMATION ON DELEGATION'S VISIT

A. Membership of US Oil Delegation

W.W. Keeler, Executive Vice-President, Phillips Petroleum Company, Bartlesville, Oklahoma

Ira H. Cram, Chairman of the Executive Committee, Continental Oil Company, New York, New York

George S. Dunham, Director, Socony Mobil Oil Company, Inc., New York, New York

W.M. Elias, Vice-President, Pan American Petroleum Corporation, Tulsa, Okla.

George F. Getty, II, President, Tidewater Oil Company Los Angeles, California

George T. Piercy, Executive Assistant to the President, Standard Oil Company (New Jersey) New York, New York

Neal J. Smith, Vice-President, Chevron Oil Company Houston, Texas

Noyes D. Smith, Jr., Vice-President, Shell Development Company, Houston, Texas

Robert E. Ebel, Office of Oil and Gas, Department of Interior, Washington, D.C.

Alexander Gakner, Bureau of Mines, Department of Interior, Washington, D.C.

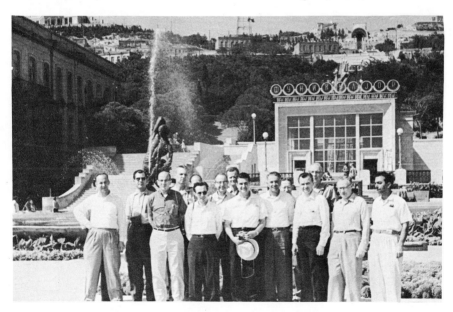

Photo No. 1. Members of the US Oil Delegation at Baku.
(left to right): D. Polyakov (GNTK member, who accompanied the delegation on its tour); George Getty, II; Robert Ebel; Whitney Elias; Alexander Gakner; Noyes Smith; Neal Smith; W.W. Keeler; M.M. Musayev (Chief Engineer of the Azerbaydzhan Petroleum Administration); Ira Cram; George Piercy; and George Dunham.

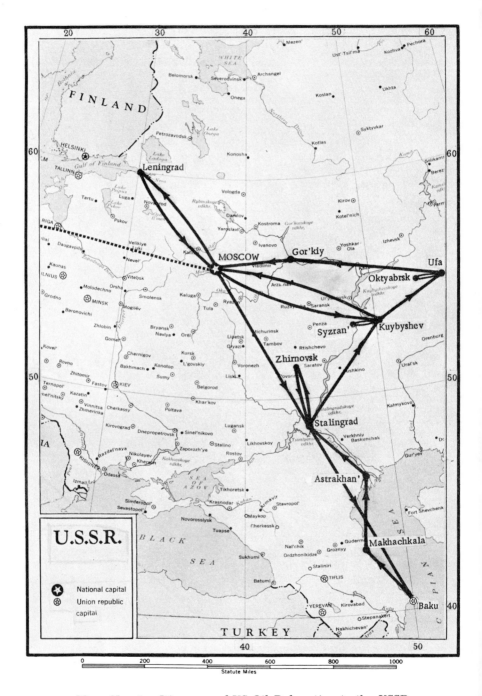

Map. No. 1. Itinerary of US Oil Delegation to the USSR

B. Itinerary of the US Oil Delegation

August, 1960

2		Arrived in Moscow by plane
3	(Moscow)	Meeting with State Scientific and Technical Committee (GNTK) on itinerary; sightseeing
4	(Moscow)	Visit to All-Union Permanent Exhibition of Science and Industry; reception at U.S. Embassy
5	(Moscow)	Institute for the Design of Oil Refineries (Gipronefte-zavad)
6	(Moscow)	All-Union Scientific and Research Institute on Crude Oil (VNIINEFT')
7	(Moscow)	Sightseeing
8	(Ufa)	Moscow-Ufa by plane
9	(Ufa)	The Ufa Scientific Research Institute on Crude Oil and Natural Gas (UFNIING)
10	(Ufa)	Novo-Ufa refinery; night train from Ufa to Oktyabrsk
11		Tuymazy-Oktyabrsk oil fields; night train return to Ufa
12	(Moscow)	Ufa-Moscow by plane
13	Moscow)	Meeting with Gosplan
14	(Baku)	Moscow-Baku by plane
15	(Baku)	Novo-Baku refinery; movie on Neftyanyye Kamni offshore oil fields
16	(Baku)	Karadag oil fields
17	(Baku)	Artyom offshore oil field
18	(Stalingrad)	Baku-Stalingrad by plane. Meeting with Stalingrad Scientific and Research Institute on Crude Oil and Natural Gas (SNIING).
19	(Zhirnovsk)	Stalingrad-Zhirnovsk by plane; Zhirnovsk oil field
20	(Stalingrad)	Zhirnovsk-Stalingrad by plane; visit with Stalingrad Council of National Economy (SOVNARKHOZ)
21	(Stalingrad)	Sightseeing
22	(Kuibyshev)	Stalingrad-Kuybyshev by plane; hydrofoil boat to Syzran' refinery; hydrofoil back to Kuybyshev; car to Novo-Kuybyshev
23	(Kuibyshev)	Novo-Kuybyshev refinery
24	(Leningrad)	Kuybyshev-Leningrad by plane
25	(Leningrad)	Sightseeing; conference on preparation of report on trip
26	(Leningrad)	Sightseeing
27	(Leningrad)	Production and refining conferences on preparation of reports; sightseeing
28	(Moscow)	Leningrad-Moscow by jet; shopping
29	(Moscow)	Report to State Scientific and Technical Committee (GNTK)
30	(Moscow)	Six members depart Moscow for home or other destinations; remaining four have conference with Soyuz-nefteexport
31		Depart Moscow. End of tour.

C. Some Impressions on the USSR

Although the primary objective of the visit of the delegation was to study the oil industry of the Soviet Union, some contact with the Russian people was inevitable. This contact at best was only fleeting and did not permit the members of the delegation more than scattered impressions of the people, their culture and country. These impressions are recorded here for what ever value they may have.

We were told on our flight into Moscow by a Russian reporter returning home from duties in the Congo, that we would find the Russian people to be friendly. Most were friendly, but all were extremely curious. In the major cities of Leningrad and Moscow, where the sight of Western tourists on the street has become quite common, our presence went virtually unnoticed. But as our journey took us to such places as Novo-Kuybyshevsk and Syzran', where Westerners, let alone Americans, rarely visited, we found ourselves to be the immediate centers of attraction. Crowds gathered at the refineries, at the oil fields and on the street to look at us as if we were the visiting heads of a friendly state. At Syzran', the crowds grew so large that we required the help of the police to get to our automobiles. Even as we tried to drive away the people pushed themselves into our cars to shake hands with us.

The propaganda to which the Soviet people are subjected is heavy and constant and every medium is utilized — newspapers, magazines, posters, radio and television. Each industrial installation, institute, school, Palace of Culture and the like exhibits charts comparing USSR achievements and plans to that of the US. Conversely, a considerable amount of propaganda is directed against the way we live and work, against our conveniences, and, of course, against our "unfriendly" acts. Even in the simplest mind some confusion must result from simultaneously holding us up as a goal and as a thing to scorn.

Perhaps the propaganda conflict accounts for the friendly curiosity with which the delegation was regarded. In spite of the fact that we were in the USSR at the time of the Powers trial, little rancor was evident on part of the people we met. They were anxious to hear something nice about their country but appeared politely incredulous if one mentioned statistics that were obviously beyond their experience or not in line with what they had been told, and became disturbed and changed the topic if politics were mentioned. This last tactic seemed a matter of courtesy.

Much of the interest shown in the Americans, particularly in Leningrad and Moscow, merely derived from an opportunity to practice the English language. Some of these people claimed that they listened to the Voice of America as a means for practicing their English. Content of the program did not have much meaning. These listeners enjoyed the music but were both bored and puzzled by the religious tinge. They could not correlate our assertions of having achieved world leadership in materialistic success with any religious devotion.

A custom extensively practiced throughout the Soviet Union is the exchanging of pins, medals or small trinkets with foreign visitors. Usually the small children in the street were the first to offer some small gift, and greatly appreciated a small remembrance of America in return. Adults were particularly embarrased if they could not offer something in return. An incident such as this took place during a hydrofoil boat trip along the Volga River from Kuybyshev to Syzran'. The waitress at the snackbar on the boat discovered that she had no tea. It so happened that one of the delegation had a small package with him, which he presented to her. Her profuse thanks were accepted and no more was thought of it. When we reboarded the boat that evening for the return trip to Kuybyshev, the waitress presented to the delegation a box of chocolates, which probably represented a full day's salary for her.

That the Soviet Union has accomplished much in the 40-odd years since the revolution cannot be denied. These accomplishments were apparent in the jet plane, the TU-104, which the delegation had occasion to use, and in the successful launching of the earth satellite which took place during our stay in the USSR. Also apparent, however, was the fact that such achievements in one phase of the Soviet economy have been at the expense of what would have been a higher standard of living for the Soviet citizen, had some of this energy been channeled in this direction. The Soviet citizen may recognize that his standard of living is comparatively low, but in looking back, he realizes that some progress has been made. Justification seems to be found in that his country is so young that time has not been sufficient to develop fully in all respects. Only in one city did the members of the delegation have an opportunity to visit the homes of our hosts in the Soviet Union. One man, his wife, and two children shared one room, approximately 12 feet by 18 feet. On the other hand, another professional man, his wife, daughter and mother had a comfortable but plain apartment with a small library. The floor space and conveniences available to even the higher-ranking workers would hardly satisfy an American. Housing is one of the most severe problems facing the Soviet government, but fulfillment of the Seven Year Plan goals will do little more than keep up with the growth in population and urbanization. Quality in construction has been sacrificed for

Photo No. 2. Housing in the City of Ufa — The Old.

Photo No. 3. Housing in the City of Ufa — The New.

speed, consequently, the building standards would be unacceptable in many countries.

Our hosts made every effort to secure for us the best in hotel and travel accomodations, in food, and in entertainment. We attended a ballet in Leningrad, a football game in Moscow and had the opportunity to view the world-famous Obratsev puppets. In Novo-Kuybyshevsk we were guests at a highly professional performance of folk music and dancing given by workers from the local oil refinery, and in Ufa we attended a performance of a traveling opera company from Sverdlovsk. Such performances were always well-attended, and the restaurants where we dined were always crowded until late in the evening.

Yet one could not dispel the knowledge that the Soviet Union still is a police state, although the man on the street is accustomed to this police state to such an extent that he professes it is one no longer. To complaints about having our rooms searched and about surveillance on the street there were no answers. But the sum of all that our group saw, heard, and sensed during our trip leads to the conclusion that, however distasteful the Soviet system is to Americans and however unpalatable the methods used to make this system work may be, the Communist leaders, including the business men the delegation visited, are determined to make it work. They appeared convinced that the Soviet Union some day will be the leading country in the world.

II. ENERGY IN THE USSR
AND THE ROLE OF PETROLEUM

As determined by Soviet policy in effect through the Fifth Five Year Plan (1951-55), coal has had a predominant and rising share in the fuels and energy balance and petroleum has had a small and declining share. The so-called "mineralization" of the fuel balance, or the sharp rise in the relative share of hard coal, was the principal feature in the expansion of the fuels and energy industry. Emphasis had been given to the development of local, low-quality fuels, to the development of regional self-sufficiency in terms of fuel, and to the expansion of production of synthetic fuels, primarily for the purpose of reducing long hauls of natural fuels, particularly petroleum. In fact, a strong effort had been made to eliminate residual fuel oil entirely from the fuel balance and in its place, to transfer the important branches of industry to the consumption of solid fuels. The energy balance of the USSR for the years 1932, 1940, and 1950 is shown in Table 1.

Table 1

The Energy Balance of the USSR
1932, 1940, and 1950

(Converted to Standard Fuel and
Expressed as a Percent of the Total)

Source of Energy	1932	1940	1950
Coal	50.8	58.6	64.6
Crude Oil	28.7	18.5	17.0
Natural Gas	1.3	1.8	2.3
Shale	0.1	0.2	0.4
Peat	5.1	5.7	4.6
Fuelwood	13.5	14.2	8.8
Hydroelectric Power .	0.5	1.0	2.3
Total	100.0	100.0	100.0

First evidence of dissatisfaction in the USSR with the share which petroleum held in the fuels and energy balance came in May of 1955. At that time an article was published in Pravda, signed by a relatively obscure author, in which was stressed the importance of increasing the share of crude oil and natural gas in the fuels and energy balance. It is not clear what prompted the decision for a shift in priority from coal to crude oil and natural gas. Surely a number of economic factors — reduced capital investment and reduced cost per unit of output and a higher index of labor productivity — weighed heavily, but strategic and political decisions also must have supported this shift. In any case, justification and framework for the shift in the fuels and energy balance which followed had been established.

To effect the planned shift in production of energy in the USSR, a shift in the allocation of capital investment in the energy sector was also necessary. This meant that, to increase the share of petroleum in the energy balance, investments in this sector would have to be proportionately larger. During the period 1952-58 productive investment in the coal, electric power, crude oil and natural gas industries totalled 208 billion 1955 rubles. Of this, the coal industry absorbed more than 29 percent, the petroleum industry almost 35 percent, and the electric power industry 36 percent. The plan for the subsequent seven-year period, during which the shift in production of energy is to become more pronounced, called for the crude oil and natural gas industries to absorb substantially larger shares and the coal industry a much smaller share, of total investment during 1959-65, than they respectively absorbed during 1952-58. Little change is planned for the relative share of productive investment allocated to the electric power industry, but the share for the crude oil and natural gas industries is to be increased to more than 56 percent, while that for coal is to decline to about 20 percent. More illustrative are the relationships of the magnitudes of the expenditures. During the period 1959-65 compared with 1952-58, the productive investment in the gas industry is to increase by 335 percent and that in the crude oil industry by about 108 percent, while the productive investment in the coal industry shows only a relatively small increase of 25 percent. Investments in the various branches of the energy sector of the economy for the period 1952-58 are compared with those planned for 1959-65 in Table 2.

Table 2

Productive Investment in the Soviet Energy Economy,
by Selected Branch

1952-58 and 1959-65

Branch	1952-1958		1959-1965	
	Billion 1955 Rubles	Percent of Total	Billion 1955 Rubles	Percent of Total
Coal	61.2	29.4	75 *	20.2
Crude Oil.	62.7	30.1	130.2	35.0
Natural Gas . . .	9.5	4.6	41.3	11.0
Electric Power .	75.1	36.1	125 **	33.5
Total	208.5	100.0	371.5	100.0

*The Seven Year Plan states a range of 75-80 billion rubles. The low side of the range has been selected.

**For 1959-65, a range of 125-129 billion rubles has been given. The low side of the range has been used in this computation.

In terms of short-range effects upon the national economy of the USSR, the shift in the fuels and energy balance will be of little significance. To be sure, some localities will benefit immensely with the completion of natural gas pipelines and the subsequent reduction of dependence upon expensive coals and local fuels such as peat and fuelwood. Also, some savings in capital investment and labor, in addition to a higher rate of growth in the production of energy, will be apparent on a year-to-year basis.

Analysis of the long-range benefits which will accrue to the Soviet economy makes clear the purposes for which the energy shift has been planned. Most important among these benefits are (1) increased labor productivity in the energy sector of the economy; (2) reduced capital investment per comparable unit of output; (3) a savings in fuel by means of increased efficiency in combustion of petroleum fuels compared with solid fuels and therefore a reduction in cost per unit of output or of work done; (4) a savings in time in the development of comparable productive capacity; and (5) an increased exportable surplus of energy in a readily marketable form.

During the 10-year period 1955-65, the extraction of primary energy in the USSR is to increase from about 490 million tons* of standard fuel to more than 1,130 million tons. Increases for all sources of energy are planned, but the most rapid growth will be in the production of crude oil and natural gas. By 1965 more than one-half of total energy production in the USSR will be in the form of crude oil and natural gas. As shown in Table 3, the production of crude oil and natural gas combined is to increase to 49.4 percent of total energy output by 1965, compared with 30.7 percent in 1958 and only 22.9 percent in 1955.

Continuation of the shift in the fuel balance during the Seven Year Plan is expected to result in considerable savings for the national economy, according to preliminary calculations by Soviet economists. These savings, in production, in transportation, and in end use, are to total more than 125 billion rubles (US $31.25 billion)**. Labor input per metric ton of standard fuel is to decline from 0.958 man-days in 1958 to 0.710 man-days in 1965***. Concomitantly, the average weighted cost of production of a metric ton of standard fuel is to decline from 73 rubles, 58 kopecks to 57 rubles, 79 kopecks. The cost of production of a ton of standard fuel of energy in the USSR in 1961 is planned at about 64 rubles.

During the 10-year period 1955-65, some shifts in the consumption of energy within the various consuming sectors will take place. The electric power stations are to become the largest consumers of energy in the USSR, replacing all other industry as a whole. On the other hand, consumption by transport and construction materials as a share of the national total is to decline, largely reflecting a transfer to liquid and gaseous fuels. Only a slight growth is predicted for "industry", and slight declines are anticipated in the consumption of energy in agriculture and in the communal-everyday sector. For all consumers during the period, however, the total consumption of energy is to increase by 80 percent, from 515 million tons of standard fuel to 930 million tons. Data illustrating the shifts in energy consumption during 1955-65 are given in Table 4.

As a guide for future planning, Soviet authorities have established control estimates for the production of crude oil, natural gas and coal through 1980. These goals, shown on page 11, serve only as support for long-range planning affecting all sectors of the national economy and are not official annual goals.

------

*All tons in this report are metric tons.

**See Table of Conversions, p. iv, for ruble-dollar exchange rate.

***In this calculation and in that for costs, labor inputs and costs of production for all types of fuels were held constant for 1959-65.

Table 3

Reported, Estimated and Planned Production of Primary Energy in the USSR
1955, 1958-60, and 1965

Source	Unit of Natural Measure	1955			1958			1959			1960			1965 Plan		
		Natural Units	Standard fuel MMT	% of Total	Natural Units	Standard fuel MMT	% of Total	Natural Units	Standard fuel MMT	% of Total	Natural Units	Standard fuel MMT	% of Total	Natural Units	Standard fuel MMT	% of Total
Coal	MMT	391.2	310.8	63.2	496.1	362.1	56.9	506.6	370.0	54.4	513	384.8	52.2	612	475	42.0
Crude Oil	MMT	70.8	101.2	20.6	113.2	161.9	25.4	129.5	185.3	27.3	148	211.6	28.7	265*	379	33.5
Natural Gas	BCM	9.0	11.4	2.3	28.1	33.9	5.3	35.4	42.5	6.3	45.1	54.2	7.4	148.3	180	15.9
Peat	MMT	50.8	20.8	4.2	53.3	21.1	3.3	60.5	23.0	3.4	56.4	21.4	2.9	71.4	26.6	2.4
Shale	MMT	10.8	3.3	0.7	13.2	4.5	0.7	13.7	4.7	0.7	14.0	4.8	0.7	21.0	6.0	0.5
Fuelwood	MMT	–	32.4	6.6	–	32.9	5.2	–	33.9	5.0	–	34	4.6	–	25	2.2
Mineral Fuel Total		–	479.9	97.6	–	616.4	96.8	–	659.4	97.0	–	710.8	96.5	–	1,091.6	96.5
Hydroelectric power	BKH	23.2	11.6	2.4	46.5	20.4	3.2	47.6	20.5	3.0	56.2	26	3.5	102.5	40	3.5
Grand Total		–	491.5	100.0	–	636.8	100.0	–	679.9	100.0	–	736.8	100.0	–	1,131.6	100.0

*Estimate

MMT — Million Metric Tons.   BCM — Billion Cubic Meters.   BKH — Billion Kilowatt-hours.

Type of fuel	1970–72*	1975	1980
Crude oil (million tons)	350–400	480	600
Natural gas (billion cubic meters)	270–320	500	650
Coal (million tons)	650–750	900	1,000

*Only recently new estimates of probable production of the major sources of energy in the USSR by 1972 have appeared in the Soviet press, based apparently on performance achieved in the first 2 years of the Seven Year Plan. These revised estimates are as follows: Coal: 750–765 million tons; Crude Oil: 430–450 million tons; Natural Gas: 320–330 billion cubic meters. If these estimates are accepted, then comparatively higher levels of production may be anticipated for 1975.

Table 4

Shifts in the Consumption of Energy in the USSR by Consumer

1955 and 1965

Consumer	1955		1965	
	Million Metric Tons of Standard Fuel	Percent of Total	Million Metric Tons of Standard Fuel	Percent of Total
Industry	150	29.5	290	31.0
Electric Power Stations	125	24.5	310	33.5
Transport and Construction Materials	120	23.0	150	16.0
Communal Economy of Cities	50	9.5	80	8.5
Agriculture	70	13.5	100	11.0
Total	515*	100.0	930	100.0

*Includes decentralized gathering of fuels, i.e., the gathering of wood and other local fuels by the population.

The USSR is striving to achieve an energy balance, resembling that presently in the US, wherein fuel supplies are furnished in part by each of the major sources of energy (crude oil, natural gas and coal). To coordinate the development of a more rational fuel balance, a special commission, attached to Gosplan, USSR, was created in 1959. This commission will be responsible for the unification of plans for the production and consumption of primary energy in the USSR.

By 1972, Soviet planning experts hope to have achieved some degree of success in this respect. One such authority has pictured the energy balance of the USSR in that year to be as follows (in standard fuel, as a percent of the total):

Source of Energy	1972
Coal	32. 2
Crude Oil	34. 4
Natural gas	23. 3
Peat	2. 4
Shale	0 6
Fuelwood	1. 3
Hydroelectric power	2. 6
Atomic energy	3. 2
Total	100. 0

Except for the share of atomic energy, which probably is overstated, this structure is representative of both current Soviet plans and capabilities.

III. ORGANIZATION AND CONTROL

A. General

The organization of administration of the petroleum industry of the USSR has undergone numerous changes since the end of World War II. Division of the fuel industry of the Soviet Union into branches of coal and petroleum and the subsequent creation of a People's Commissariat of the Petroleum Industry had taken place in 1939. This organ continued to function until 1946, when two independent central organs were established. One, the Ministry of the Petroleum Industry for the Southern and Western Regions, was to bring the production of crude oil in these areas up to the prewar level, and higher. The second, the Ministry of the Petroleum Industry for the Eastern Regions, was to create a new center of production of crude oil in the USSR. By the end of 1948, sufficient progress had been made in both directions that it became more expedient to establish a single center of administration of all branches of the petroleum industry, which led to the establishment of the Ministry of the Petroleum Industry, USSR.

In 1954, the Ministry of the Petroleum Industry, USSR, was changed from an all-union to a union-republic status, with the creation of the Ministry of the Petroleum Industry, Azerbaydzhan SSR, and the transfer to this new ministry of control of all oil enterprises, organizations and installations in the republic.

In the following year, because of the vast amount of construction being undertaken in the petroleum industry and the number of inherent problems, a Ministry of Construction of Enterprises of the Petroleum Industry was formed from the construction organizations and enterprises of the union-republic Ministry of the Petroleum Industry.

Until September of 1956, the Ministry of the Petroleum Industry, USSR, had also been responsible for the development of the natural gas industry through the auspices of the Main Administration for Petroleum and Natural Gas, one of a total of 17 Main Administrations under the Ministry through which the functions of the Ministry were carried out. At that time there was announced the creation of a new administrative organ — the Main Administration for the Gas Industry (Glavgaz) — which was attached directly to the Council of Ministers, USSR. Included among the responsibilities delegated to Glavgaz were the transportation of natural and manufactured gases, the production of manufactured gas, construction of transmission gas pipelines, and geological and drilling work. Later these responsibilities were expanded to include the construction of trunk crude oil and petroleum product pipelines.

Dissolution of the Main Administration for Petroleum and Natural Gas reduced the number of main administrations under the Ministry of the Petroleum Industry, USSR, to 16. The remaining main administrations were as follows:

Ministry of the Petroleum Industry, USSR (1957)

Petroleum Production in Eastern Regions	Petroleum Production in Western Regions
Geophysical Operations	Prospecting for Crude Oil and Natural Gas
Planning	Petroleum Prospecting
Supply	Power Supply
Technical Material Supply	Workers' Supply
Refining	Machine Building
Sale and Transport of Crude and Products	Petroleum Refining and Synthetic Fuels
Educational Institutions	Personnel and Wages

Each of the two main administrations concerned with the production of crude oil was divided into regional petroleum associations, one association for each major geographical area in which crude oil was produced, for example, the Bashkir Petroleum Association under the Main Administration for Petroleum Production in the Eastern Regions and the Ukrainian Petroleum Association under the Main Administration for Petroleum Production in the Western Regions. These associations were then divided into oil field administrations and drilling trusts, which in turn were subdivided into oil fields and field-supporting enterprises and into drilling offices.

Although the Ministry of the Petroleum Industry, Azerbaydzhan SSR, was a separate entity and operated independently of the union-ministry, it probably was dependent for production and drilling on the Main Administration for Petroleum Production in the Western Regions. The subordination within this ministry was basically similar to that of the union-republic ministry, with the exception of the existence of a Main Administration for Offshore Petroleum Production.

On 1 July 1957 the Administration of most of industry and construction in the Soviet Union was reorganized. Included among those affected were the Ministry of Construction of Enterprises of the Petroleum Industry, the Ministry of the Petroleum Industry, USSR, and the Ministry of the Petroleum Industry, Azerbaydzhan SSR, although the latter was changed but little and and was reestablished on a republic level.*

Both the Ministry of Construction of Enterprises of the Petroleum Industry and the Ministry of the Petroleum Industry, USSR, were abolished and, in general, responsibilities were given over to the local sovnarkhoz (Sovet Narodnogo Khozyaystva), regional councils of national economy established along existing territorial-administrative boundaries. An exception was the transfer intact of the Main Administration of Sale and Transport of Crude and Products (Glavneftesbyt) to Gosplan, USSR. Most of the regional petroleum associations were changed to petroleum administrations subordinate to the respective sovnarkhoz. Thus, for example, the Saratov Petroleum Association became the Administration of Petroleum and Gas Industry under the Saratov sovnarkhoz. In some instances, apparently in areas of relatively insignificant production of crude oil, the petroleum enterprises were merged with other fuels or ores. The relationship of the sovnarkhoz to republic-level and all-union Councils of Ministers is illustrated in Figures 1 and 2.

B. Regional

The sovnarkhoz is the core of regional planning in the USSR. The flow of economic planning in the USSR is shown in Figure 3, which depicts the relationship of the sovnarkhoz to the local enterprise and to Gosplan, USSR. The construction of an annual plan is carried out in the following manner: The planning department of the local enterprise draws up a first draft covering activities for the following year. This plan is submitted to Gosplan, sovnarkhoz, which may or may not revise the plan before sending it up to Gosplan, union-republic. Usually, revisions are made at each stage as the plan becomes more general in nature and as the needs and requirements become wider in scope. Experts are called in at the various levels to provide substantive support. Finally, at Gosplan, USSR, the plan of the local enterprise indirectly is fitted into that for the country as a whole. The revised plan then is sent back through channels to the local enterprise, which, if the revised plan is found untenable, may appeal. Ordinarily, these revised plans are accepted without question.

Recently, so-called "giant" sovnarkhozy were established in the RSFSR, the Ukraine, and Kazkhstan. Originally, these republics had been given more than one sovnarkhoz. Subsequent experience showed, however, that the existence of more than one sovnarkhoz called for a tremendous amount of coordination within the republic and that the time and effort expended in this coordination by Republic Gosplans led to inadequate attention to planning responsibilities. To correct this situation, a "giant" or single sovnarkhoz was created for each of these republics, to stand alongside of the republic Gosplan. Generally, the republic Gosplan handles production planning and

---

*Only to be abolished in July, 1959, and responsibilities transferred to the republic sovnarkhoz.

Fig. 1. Organization and Planning in the RSFSR*, Locating Those Bodies of Interest to the US Oil Delegation

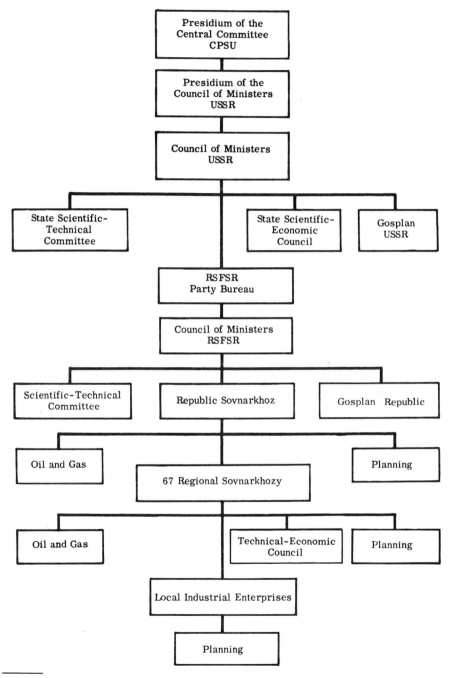

*Also applicable to the Ukraine and Kazakhstan.

Fig. 2

Typical Structure of Organization and Planning in a Republic*,
Locating Those Bodies of Interest to the US Oil Delegation

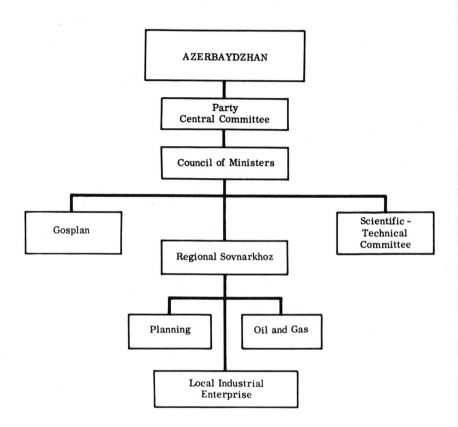

the republic sovnarkhoz handles sales and supply and other coordination
tasks.

C. National

The responsibilities for the planning of the development of the national
economy of the USSR rest with two organizations — Gosplan and Gosekonomsovet, both attached to the USSR Council of Ministers. The structures
of these organizations are depicted in Figure 4. Gosplan is responsible for
short-range planning and expends most of its effort in the construction of

---

*But not applicable to the Ukraine, the RSFSR, or Kazakhstan, where there
is more than one regional sovnarkhoz.

Fig. 3

Flow of Economic Planning in the USSR

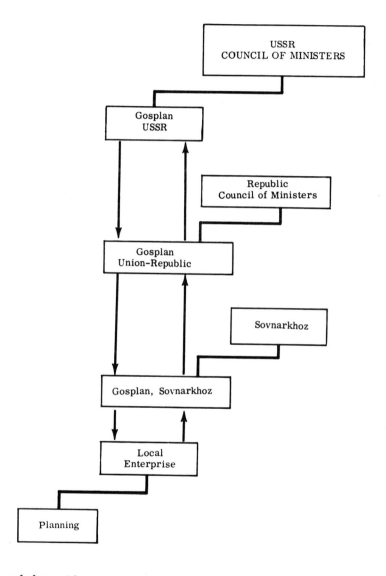

the annual plan, with some attention given to the next 5-year period. Gosekonomsovet (the State Scientific-Economic Council) has as its function that of
long-range planning, that is, planning for 5-7 years and beyond.

Gosekonomsovet was created in April, 1958, but little was known of its
functions and responsibilities until July, 1960, when it was noted in the
Soviet press that this organ had been given long-range planning duties.
Prior to the creation of Gosekonomsovet, both short-range and long-range

Fig. 4

Structures of Gosplan, USSR and Gosekonomsovet, USSR

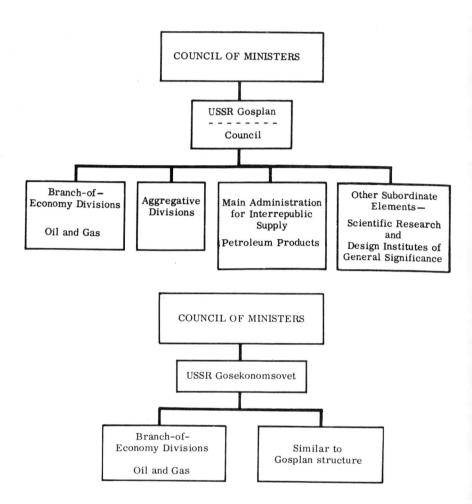

planning responsibilities had been concentrated in Gosplan. The full scope of duties of Gosekonomsovet is not clear at present, but it is evident that Gosplan and Gosekonomsovet enjoy equal status.

Both Gosplan and Gosekonomsovet have branch-of-economy divisions and in each of these divisions is a section devoted to the oil and gas industries. These sections are responsible for general development of oil and gas, both current and future.

D. Marketing

Prior to World War II, the marketing of petroleum products in the USSR was handled through Glavneftesbyt — the Main Administration for Petroleum

Marketing. This organ, attached to the People's Commissariat of the Petroleum Industry, planned the movement of goods, the use of resources, organized warehouse deliveries, and handled the bookkeeping and accounting.

During the war, the more important glavsbyts (Main Marketing Administrations) were renamed glavsnabs (Main Supply Administration) and were placed under the control of the Council of People's Commissars. Thus, Glavneftesbyt became Glavneftesnab (The Main Administration for Petroleum Supply). This move facilitated the rigid centralization of the placing of orders by the consumer and of planned deliveries from the supplier.

At the close of the war, Glavneftesnab was renamed Glavneftesbyt and control once again was given to the Ministry of the Petroleum Industry, which had replaced the People's Commissariat of the Petroleum Industry. But in 1947 it was again renamed Glavneftesnab and was attached to the Council of Ministers, USSR. In 1948, all of the glavsnabs, which included those controlling coal, petroleum products, forest products and light industry, were placed under a newly created government committee — Gossnab, USSR — which handled all the planning and operational work involved in the supplying and marketing of these products.

About 6 months later Glavneftesnab and the others were transferred back to the appropriate ministries and renamed glavsbyts. In 1953, Gossnab, USSR was merged with Gosplan, USSR and the latter assumed all of the planning and distribution functions of the former. This system continued to function until July of 1957, when, as a part of the reorganization of industry in the USSR, the Ministry of the Petroleum Industry was abolished.

The reorganization of industry in the USSR lasted well over a year. During this period and in order to ensure the uninterrupted delivery of material, Glavneftesbyt was transferred from the then-abolished Ministry of the Petroleum Industry to Gosplan, USSR.

Once the government was confident that the gosplans of the union-republics and the sovnarkhozy were able to fulfill their responsibilities, reorganization of the marketing system took place, in the middle of 1958. Glavneftesbyt was reorganized into Soyuzglavneft — the Main Administration for Interrepublic Delivery of Petroleum Products, attached to Gosplan, USSR. The structure of Soyuzglavneft' is shown in Figure 5. In addition to the creation of Soyuzglavneft' on the national level, petroleum marketing organs were established in the union-republics. In the republics of the Ukraine, Moldavia, Uzbek, Kazakstan, and Kirgiz, these organs were attached to the Gosplan of the republic. In the RSFSR, Lithuania, and in Tadzhik, the marketing organ was attached to the Council of Ministers of the republic. Finally, in White Russia, Georgia, Azerbaydzhan, Latvia, Estonia, Turkmen, and Armenia, the organ is subordinated to the sovnarkhoz of the republic.

The functions of these organs, glavsnabsbyts, are basically planning and regulatory. The main function of Soyuzglavneft' is the development of plans for delivery between republics and deliveries for the needs of the country as a whole. In addition, Soyuzglavneft' plans the shipments to and from republics for export and to government storage reserves, and the distribution of imports according to republic.

Fig. 5

Structure of Soyuzglavneft' — the Main Administration
for Interrepublic Deliveries of Petroleum Products

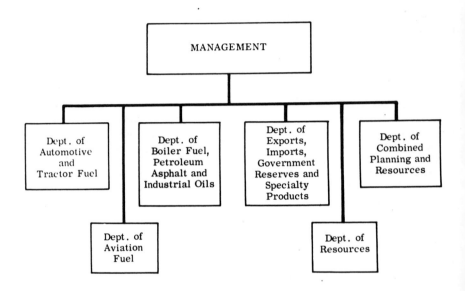

IV. CAPITAL INVESTMENT

Capital investments in the oil and gas industries of the USSR during the postwar period have represented a rather significant portion of total investment in the national economy. A total of almost 101 billion rubles, the equivalent of slightly more than $US 25 billion, reportedly was invested in these industries during the years 1946–58. These sums represented about 5.6 percent of total investment in the national economy during 1946–50 and 6.7 percent during 1952–58. Estimated productive capital investment in the oil and gas industries, by sector, during 1946–58 is shown in Table 5.

Analysis of the capital investments during 1946–58 indicates that of the 101 billion ruble total, 63 percent was invested in oil extraction, including drilling. By individual year, however, investment in this sector has been declining, from 76.7 percent of the total in 1950 to 56.1 percent in 1958. For the entire 7-year period 1959–65, investment in oil extraction is to represent only 42 percent of total investment in the oil and gas industries.

Little information is available on investment in oil refining and on petrochemical installations constructed at refinery sites. It is known that there has been a sharp change in the share of capital investment in this sector. During the Fifth Five Year Plan (1951–55) a rapid growth took place in investment in refining, but the increase in the relative share occurred primarily as the result of construction of synthetic liquid fuel installations, representing 9.2 percent of total capital investment. These synthetic liquid fuel installations have proved to be uneconomical. They require very high average capital investments and exploitation expenditures per unit of output.

Table 5

Productive Capital Investment in the Oil and Gas Industries of the USSR, by sector

1946-58

(Millions of Rubles in 1 July 1955 Prices)

	1946	1950	1946-50	1955	1951-55	1956	1957	1958	1952-58
Oil Industry									
Extraction Phase									
Exploratory and Development Drilling	643	2,754	8,172	3,667	17,133	3,357	3,670	4,590	25,700
Production	795	1,977	6,395	2,300	11,834	2,465	2,830	2,930	17,500
Total	1,438	4,731	14,567	5,967	28,967	5,822	6,500	7,520	43,200
Refining, Transport and Storage*	345	1,325	3,778	2,886	13,806	2,545	2,600	3,040	19,500
Total Oil Industry	1,783	6,056	18,345	8,853	42,773	8,367	9,100	10,560	62,700
Gas Industry									
Extraction Phase									
Exploratory and Development Drilling	-	-	-	414	1,588	425	630	825	3,300
Production Total } Transport	103	113	629	569	2,334	1,156	1,590	2,015	6,200
Total Gas Industry	103	113	629	983	3,922	1,581	2,220	2,840	9,500
Total Oil and Gas Industries	1,886	6,169	18,974	9,836	46,695	9,948	11,320	13,400	72,200

*Calculated as a residual.

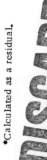

At the present time these installations have been combined with crude oil refineries and petrochemical units. In this manner, the capital investments of the Fourth and Fifth Five Year Plans, covering 1946-55, will have served to foster a more rapid expansion of petrochemical synthesis during 1959-65.

The relative share of capital investment in oil refining and petrochemical production showed a decline during 1956-58, although in absolute terms the investment remained at about the same level. This decline largely reflected underfulfillment of investment plans rather than any pre-designed reduction.

Investment during the entire postwar period 1946-58 by geographic area and related to the increment in crude oil extraction, underlines the extremely high return in production per unit of investment in the Urals-Volga.

Area	Capital Investment as a Percent of the Total		Increment in Crude Oil Extraction as a Percent of the Total
Caucasus	38.4		13.0
Including:			
Azerbaydzhan . .		23.1	5.3
Urals-Volga	38.2		79.0
Including:			
Tatar ASSR		10.2	30.4
Bashkir ASSR . .		12.3	23.3
Kuybyshev Oblast		7.2	16.3
Saratov Oblast . .		3.0	3.0
Stalingrad Oblast		2.0	4.0
Other		3.5	2.0
Central Asia	12.4		6.0
Other	11.0		2.0
Totals . . .	100.0		100.0

Distribution by geographic area of the total investment in the oil and gas industry in 1958 shows the following pattern:

Area	Percent of Total
Caucasus	23.6
Urals-Volga	45.8
Central Asia	12.3
Other	18.3
Total	100.0

Thus, in the effort to provide for the growth of production of crude oil at the highest rate possible, and to take advantage of the maximum return available, capital investment in the Urals-Volga has been stepped up sharply.

Capital investment in the oil and gas industry during the Seven Year Plan is planned at 170-173 billion rubles ($US 42.5-43.25 billion), compared with 72.2 billion rubles in the preceding 7-year period 1952-58. Of the total designated for 1959-65, about 41 billion rubles, or approximately 24 percent, will be invested in the natural gas industry, almost one-half of which has been set aside for the construction of natural gas pipelines. The estimated distribution of the planned productive capital investment in the oil and gas industry during 1959-65, compared with those sums invested during 1952-58, is presented in Table 6.

It should be noted that the 170-173 billion ruble total represents only productive investment and therefore excludes expenditures on housing, welfare and the like. In addition, the investment in the natural gas industry includes those sums designated for construction of natural gasoline plants. Similarly, if a petrochemical plant is to be built within a crude oil refinery,

Table 6

Estimated Productive Investment in the Oil and Natural Gas
Industries of the USSR, by Sector of Industry
1952-58 and 1959-65
(In comparable prices)

	1952-58		1959-65	
	Billion Rubles	% of Total	Billion Rubles	% of Total
Oil				
Oil Extraction				
Exploratory and Development Drilling	25.7	35.6	43.0	25.1
Extraction	17.5	24.2	29.0	16.9
Total	43.2	59.8	72.0	42.0
Refining (including petrochemical installations at refineries) and Storage	} 19.5	} 27.0	38.0	22.6
Pipeline Construction			20.0	11.7
Grand Total	62.7	86.8	130.2	75.9
Natural Gas				
Gas Extraction				
Exploratory and Development Drilling	3.3	4.6	13.0	7.6
Extraction	2.5	3.5	6.9	4.0
Total	5.8	8.0	19.9	11.6
Pipeline Construction	3.7	5.2	17.7	10.3
Other (primarily storage)	0	0	3.7	2.2
Grand Total	9.5	13.2	41.3	24.1
Total, Oil and Natural Gas	72.2	100.0	171.5*	100.0

*Midpoint of the range of 170-173 billion rubles as stated in the Seven Year Plan.

then that investment is included in the total for the refinery. Generally speaking though, the petrochemical plants are built outside the refinery gates and therefore are not included in the refinery investments.

Available data show that at least in the years 1959-60 capital investment in the oil and gas industries has been below plan as indicated in Table 7.

Table 7

Planned and Estimated Productive Capital Investment
in the Oil and Gas Industries of the USSR
1959-61

(Billions of Rubles, in Comparable Prices)

| Sector | 1959 | | 1960 | | 1961 |
	Plan	Actual	Plan	Actual	Plan
Oil	na	12.6	na	13.6	15.6
Gas	na	3.5	na	4.1	4.9
Total	17.3	16.1	18.5	17.7	20.5

Most of these shortfalls may be attributed to the failure to construct new refining capacity and, to a lesser extent, to the lags in petroleum pipeline installation and in construction of new storage facilities. Although construction and installation trusts had the necessary capital, failure of industry to produce the required material and equipment prevented the investment of these sums.

It was very apparent that the Soviet economists with whom the delegation had an opportunity to meet had no system for relating capital expenditure and volume of production. It was also apparent that in an oil field the planners would allocate as much investment as necessary to secure the maximum production (consistent, of course, with reasonable conservation) and no evaluation of capital investment versus volume would be made. This concept falls within the general line of thinking which dominates the development of the USSR oil industry: the maximum extraction and the maximum recovery within the shortest period of time.

V. PRICING

A. The Zonal Pricing System

For the marketing of virtually all of the major petroleum products, the USSR is divided into 5 price zones in which prices vary because of differences in production costs, the turnover tax* and transport charges. The lowest price for a product is charged in Zone I, and a progressively higher price is charged in the remaining four zones as the average distance from Zone I increases. These price zones are shown on Map No. 2.

---

*The turnover tax, which is a major source of income, is actually the Soviet version of the US sales tax, but is levied at the wholesale, rather than the retail, level.

The prices for petroleum products sold in these five zones are those which were established on 1 July 1955. These prices are wholesale-release prices f.o.b. the oil base of the Main Administration of Sales, the station of designation within the Ministry of Transportation (Railroads), or the port of destination. It is believed that these zonal prices are still in effect and will remain in effect until the major new oil refining centers at Omsk and Irkutsk (Angarsk) are in full operation. At that time, it is probable that the zonal pricing system will be altered to reflect the changes in average lengths of haul resulting from the creation of new centers of refining closer to the consumer. Zonal prices for selected petroleum products are given in Table 8.

Available Soviet prices for petroleum products reflect the cost of production, the cost of transportation, and the cost of operating sales bases. Prices for some unspecified products include the turnover tax as well as administrative surcharge. The latter, however, usually is less than 1 percent of the wholesale price. In 1955, for all petroleum products marketed in the USSR, tax payments, virtually all from the turnover tax, were equal to about 50 percent of the receipts from sales; expenses of transportation and expenses of operating sales bases were equal to about 20 percent; and the f.o.b. refinery prices combined for all products marketed were equal to only 30 percent of those receipts.

Prices of crude oil to refineries are made up of three elements. The first element is the cost of production of the crude oil; the second is the cost of transport of the crude from the field to the refinery; and the third and final element is a 3-5 percent profit margin added, which goes directly to the State.

B. Ruble-Dollar Price Ratios, 1955

An attempt has been made to derive ruble-dollar price ratios for 1955 for certain of the petroleum products which are common to both the US and the USSR economies. Soviet prices were adjusted to exclude transport charges; data on turnover tax and costs of operating sales bases were lacking and, therefore, these components could not be deducted from the ruble price.

Prices in Zone 1, adjusted to exclude estimated average transport charges, were used in establishing the ruble-dollar ratios because the principal refining centers of Baku and the Ural-Volga region are located in Zone I. The average length of haul of petroleum products within Zone I was estimated at 1,000 kilometers. Transport charges of 57 rubles per ton were deducted from the prices for gasoline, diesel fuel, and lubricants; 46 rubles per ton for kerosine; and 39 rubles for motor fuel and residual fuel oil.

Ruble-dollar price ratios for selected petroleum products for 1955 are given in Table 9. As shown in the examples stated, the value of the ruble ranges from 14.3 cents for automobile transmission oil to 5.4 cents for 74-octane motor gasoline.

Table 8

USSR Zonal Prices for Selected Petroleum Products
1 July 1955

Rubles/Metric Ton

Type of Product	Zone				
	I	II	III	IV	V
Tractor kerosine	292	317	340	365	420
Tractor kerosine, high octane	320	340	390	400	440
Aviation gasoline					
B-100/130	1,025	1,075	1,100	1,140	1,315
B-95/130	898	945	986	1,088	1,238
B-93/130	875	915	960	1,060	1,200
B-91/115	715	745	785	875	960
B-70	620	670	720	790	880
Automobile gasoline					
A-66	537	564	594	640	704
A-70	620	670	720	790	880
A-74	715	745	785	875	960
Not less than 56	473	550	530	576	640
Jet Fuel					
T-1	370	390	415	440	448
TS-1	370	390	415	440	448
Illuminating kerosine	370	390	415	440	448
Diesel fuel					
(light) L	292	317	324	350	420
Z	312	337	344	370	440
DL	292	317	324	350	420
DA, DZ, DS	312	337	344	370	440
(heavy) DT-1(M-3), DT-2(M-4),					
DT-3(M-5)	261	290	306	331	399
Residual fuel oil					
Fleet mazut, 12, 20	250	279	295	320	388
Fuel oil, low sulfur, 20, 40, 60,					
80, 100, with sulfur content up					
to 0.5%	245	274	290	315	383
Fuel oil, sulfurous, 20, 40, 60,					
80, 100, with sulfur content					
from 0.5% to 1%, and highly					
sulfurous 20, 40, 60, 80, 100,					
with sulfur content above 1% ..	181	204	230	259	320
Lubricants					
Auto tractor oil AK-5 (avtol 18)	740	780	830	900	1,000
Diesel oils D-11, Dp-8, Dp-11,					
Dp-14, latter 3 with additive					
AZNII TSIATIM-1) and Dp-8,					
Dp-11, and Dp-14 (all with ad-					
ditive TSIATIM-339)	1,208	1,272	1,332	1,388	1,488
Automobile transmission oil					
Axle oil L	280	300	330	390	490
Z and S	310	335	365	420	520

Table 9

Ruble-Dollar Price Ratios for Selected Petroleum Products
1955

| Product | Specifications | | Prices | | Ratio, Rubles/ Dollar |
| | | | Prices | | |
	USSR	US	Rubles per Metric ton	Dollars per Metric ton	
Avgas	B-100/130	Grade 100/130, Houston	968	65.30	14.8
	B-95/130	Average, grades 100/130 and 91/96, Houston	841	63.43*	13.3
	B-93/130	Average, grades 100/130 and 91/96, Houston	818	63.13*	13.0
	B-91/115	Average, grades 100/130 and 91/96, Houston	658	61.07*	10.8
	B-70	Grade 80, New York	563	57.97	9.7
Mogas	Average A-66, A70 A-74	70-72 octane, M, loaded, Gulf Coast cargoes	522	34.50	15.1
		83 octane, Gulf Coast cargoes	658	35.70	18.4
	Min. octane of 56	60 octane M and below Oklahoma (Group 3)	416	36.70	11.3
Kerosine	Tractor kero., high octane Illuminating kerosine	Kerosine and/or No. 1 fuel, Baton Rouge	274	33.58	8.2
		41 to 43 gravity, water white kerosine, Gulf Coast cargoes	324	30.54	10.6
	Jet Fuels T-1 and TS-1	41 to 43 gravity, water white kerosine, Gulf Coast cargoes	324	30.54	10.6
Diesel Fuel light	Average, diesel fuels L and Z	No. 2 fuel, Gulf Coast Cargoes	245	27.90	8.8
Diesel Fuel heavy	Motor fuels DT-1 (M-3) DT-2 (M-4) DT-3 (M-5)	Average of No. 4 fuel, Baltimore, and No. 5 fuel, Baltimore	222	21.79	10.2
Lubricant	Automobile transmission oil	150 Vis. No. 3 color, Tulsa	275	39.19	7.0
Residual fuel oil	Fuel oil, low sulfur, 20, 40, 60, 80, 100, with sulfur content up to 0.5%	Average of No. 2 fuel and No. 4 fuel, Baltimore	206	25.90	8.0

*Average prices vary because the prices for the two types of gasoline have been weighted by different proportions in each case.

VI. EMPLOYMENT AND WAGES

A. Employment

The petroleum industry is a leading employer of labor in the USSR. The number of workers actively engaged in drilling, production and refining phases of the industry reached to almost a quarter of a million in 1958 but therefore excludes a significant portion of the labor force in the petroleum industry. For comparison, in that year there were 700,000 workers engaged in the procurement of wood and peat, and more than 1 million in the coal industry.

As shown in Table 10, which gives the employment in these phases of the petroleum industry for the years 1950 and 1955-59, steady growths in employment have been maintained throughout this period. This increased labor

Table 10

Employment in the Petroleum Industry of the USSR*
1950 and 1955-59

| Year | Drilling | | | Production | Refining | Total |
	Exploration	Exploitation	Total			
1950	50,000	18,000	68,000	55,600	na	na
1955	54,700	19,400	74,100	65,400	na	na
1956	53,400	19,300	72,700	66,200	58,800	197,700
1957	56,100	21,100	77,200	66,800	61,200	205,200
1958	64,000	21,300	85,300	69,200	68,300	222,800
1959	na	na	na	70,600	69,400	na

*Includes only those workers actively engaged in drilling, production or refining.

input has been accompanied by increases in worker productivity. For example, productivity per worker engaged in drilling increased from 63.9 meters in 1950 to 80.7 meters in 1958. Similarly, the extraction of crude oil per worker engaged in production increased from 682 tons in 1950 to 1,835 tons in 1959. Indices of worker productivity in drilling and production for 1950 and 1955-59 are shown in Tables 11 and 12.

Table 11

Labor Productivity in Oil Drilling
in the USSR
1950 and 1955-58

Year	Meters per worker
1950	63.9
1955	67.6
1956	70.0
1957	79.8
1958	80.7

Table 12

Labor Productivity in Extraction
of Crude Oil in the USSR
1950, 1955-59

Year	Metric tons per worker
1950	682
1955	1,082
1956	1,266
1957	1,471
1958	1,637
1959	1,835

In the USSR there are on the average about 26 men assigned to each drilling unit in operation. Those workers engaged directly in drilling operations represent only 24 percent of the total labor force occupied in oil and gas drilling. The distribution of this total labor force among the various branches is as follows:

	Percent of total
Directly in drilling	24
Derrick installation	20
Supply houses	4
Pipe-turbine bases	2.5
Workshops	6
Steam-water supply	8
Drilling mud	1.5
Well cementing	4
Transport	24
Other	6
Total	100

The average number of workers engaged in the production of crude oil has been plotted against the number of wells for most of the producing areas of the country for 1956-57. The results are displayed in Table 13.

Table 13

Number of Workers Engaged in Crude Oil Production
Per Well, by Selected Area
1956-57 Average

Area		Average Number of Workers Per Well
Azerbaydzhan SSR		1.81
Ukraine SSR		1.61
Krasnodar Kray		1.69
Turkmen SSR		1.69
Kuybyshev Oblast		1.92
Saratov Oblast		2.00
Orenburg Oblast	Urals-Volga	2.52
Stalingrad Oblast		2.57
Bashkir ASSR		3.09
Tatar ASSR		3.69

It is interesting to note that the leading producing areas, Bashkir and Tatar, have the highest consumption of labor per producing well.

By US standards, labor input in virtually all phases of the Soviet petroleum industry appeared excessive to the delegation. This applies not only to field operations, but to the research institutes and refineries as well. Local authorities hastened to point out, however, that many of these apparently "excessive" workers were being trained for the near future when their services would be needed as the production of crude oil continued to increase. The salaries of these trainees were not charged to the local enterprise.

The Novo-Baku refinery, with a rated capacity of 3 million tons per year or 60,000 b/d, employs 2,000 people. Although some of these are engaged in performing maintenance and social services and in the construction of worker's housing, plus the staffing of schools, the labor excess still is quite large by US standards.

For the 3,000 wells at the Karadag gas-condensate field, a labor force of 3,500 was employed, and for the 160 wells at the Zhirnovsk oil field northwest of Stalingrad — 2,000 people. Of these, 30 percent to 40 percent were engaged in work only incidentally related to production. About 10 percent of the total were classified as engineers, geologists and equivalently trained personnel. It is probable that many of these would not meet our standards for college graduates.

Women account for a significantly high share of the labor force in the oil industry. At those refineries visited by the delegation, about 35 percent to 45 percent of the labor force were women. Not all were performing secretarial, clerical or research tasks. Some were serving as refinery unit supervisors.

B. Wages

Wages in the oil industry rank this industry as third in the Soviet Union, after the steel industry and coal mining, in terms of average salary paid. The average wage paid at a refinery was given as 1,200 rubles per month. This sum may be increased to as much as 1,800 rubles per month, depending upon experience, tenure and bonuses for exceeding plant production norms. Refinery engineers may draw 1.5-2 times this amount, and a top refinery director may be paid as much as 5,000 rubles per month, excluding bonuses for the overfulfillment of plan.

The average wage in the field is comparable to the refinery average. Production operators receive 1,800 rubles per month and drillers as high as 3,000 rubles per month, but the bulk of the less-skilled workers draw between 800-1,000 rubles.

The delegation was informed that the success or failure of an enterprise did not affect the workers' wage. Given categories are paid the same regardless of short-term economics. However, if an enterprise does exceed its quota, it may receive a bonus. Of the amount paid in the form of a bonus, 30 percent is given over to the "directors" fund. Based on agreements with the trade union, this money is spent on improving schools, the plant, rest homes, building Palaces of Culture and so forth. As a point of departure, it should be pointed out that the Palaces of Culture, which are common to virtually every enterprise, are the focal points of community activity for both young people and adults, providing facilities for social, cultural and educational gatherings. Ordinarily 20 percent of the director's fund goes for maintenance of the plant, 40 percent for improvements in social facilities, and 40 percent for workers' resorts and vacations.

The work week averages about 40 hours. In some enterprises, a shift is underway to the 35-hour work week. At the Novo-Ufa refinery, 80 percent of the workers put in a 6-hour day, but at other refineries, a 7-hour day was standard. It was said that the variance in the work-day reflected the sulfur content of the crude charge.

At one point the delegation was told that the retirement age for laboring people was 50 for men and 45 for women, for scientists, technologists and administrators — 55 for men and 50 for women. Retirement at these ages was not mandatory, but it was said that most people did. The average worker, it was said, retires with a pension on the order of two-thirds his wage with a ceiling of 1,200 rubles per month. The delegation saw little evidence in its travels which would tend to support these statements on retirement.

VII. IMPRESSIONS OF PETROLEUM RESEARCH

A. General

The delegation's visits to the All-Union Permanent Exhibition of Science and Industry, the Institute for the Design of Oil Refineries (Giproneftezavod), the All-Union Scientific and Research Institute on Crude Oil (VNIINeft'), all located in Moscow, the Ufa Scientific and Research Institute on Crude Oil and Natural Gas (UfNIING), and the Stalingrad Scientific and Research Institute on Crude Oil and Natural Gas (SNIING) constituted its contact with research in the USSR. In addition, meetings with the Stalingrad sovnarkhoz and the State Scientific and Technical Committee (GNTK) in Moscow provided further information along these lines.

Laboratories visited do not match the standards for research laboratories in the United States in the type of building, amount and kind of space per worker, or in the amount and sophistication of equipment. Safety standards are lower; for instance, no fragmentation or fire protection was in evidence around the high-pressure experimental apparatus.

Staff members met seemed well-trained and intelligent, but this observation may be discounted either way, considering the short time available and the necessity of discussing problems through an interpreter.

If the degree of crowding or personnel per piece of equipment is a criterion, the institutes are overstaffed.

The work done is aimed at practical field problems, although some on fluid flow goes further than necessary for the problems at hand. A large portion of the work can be described as technical service rather than research.

In the All-Union Permanent Exhibition of Science and Industry in Moscow, there was evidence of applied research in refining, well-logging, transportation, and storage. The most striking things shown usually turned out to be in the design stage or to have been only partially field tested. In this category were a completely automatic drill, a sand exclusion liner of sintered steel shot, flat rolled pipe which can be rolled out like ribbon and pumped up hydraulically in the field and a prefabricated tank designed for easy transportation and fabrication on arrival in the field.

At each research institute as well as at all other enterprises visited, much attention is paid to personal recognition for those making significant contributions. In the lobby of each institute are pictures of staff members with an outline of their accomplishments. It is obvious that this recognition is considered valuable by the staff and that it promotes productivity.

In the institutes and elsewhere we saw much technical literature. Current US technical journals in the petroleum field are reproduced by photo-offset methods and are widely distributed. Important articles are translated into Russian, and distributed to those who do not read English. In addition, the delegation noticed here and there technical journals, perhaps equivalent to confidential company reports in the United States. These appeared to be detailed and specific in contrast to the generalized published reports.

A fairly high percentage of the technical people the delegation met read English. There were indications that they did not always understand what they read because of lack of facility and lack of familiarity with the social framework within which the articles are written. Basically, however, it appears that the petroleum industry at least is well supplied with literature on Petroleum Technology from within and from the world at large. An example is availability of completely translated issues of a leading US oil industry journal, as shown in Figure 6.

Considering the general level of industrial and economic development in the USSR and the close control over consumer products, the Soviet need for updating through research is less than is the case in the Western world. In addition, there is relatively free access to Western research advances when they need them. It is very possible, then, that Soviet research, in petroleum and elsewhere, is not nearly as glittering as its successes in a few selected fields might indicate. The observations by the delegation while in the USSR do not preclude this possibility.

B. Notes on Institutes Visited by Delegates

1. The All-Union Permanent Exhibition of Science and Industry

The All-Union Permanent Exhibition of Science and Industry, located on the outskirts of Moscow, covers more than 500 acres and contains about 300 structures. It is well laid out in broad avenues, gardens, fountains, lakes and monuments and contains scores of buildings in styles representing particular republics, major industries and major sciences. In the regional buildings, the characteristic industrial, agricultural and cultural products are displayed. It has a world fair atmosphere except for the absence of entertainment. It does contain restaurants, outdoor soft-drink stands and piped classical and semi-classical music.

The exhibition is said to be open the year around. It maintains one hundred interpreters for the benefit of visitors. Available within each building are specialists capable of explaining the technical aspects of given portions of the exhibits. The petroleum delegation visited the oil and gas exhibit, the geological and geophysical exhibits and the plastics exhibit. Full-scale equipment, samples of products and detailed scaled models of refineries, plants and oil field equipment were very nicely displayed. Many pieces of equipment and many of the models shown are not in routine use, but are in the research or experimental stage. Equipment of more than routine interest to the delegation is described below.

a. Sand Exclusion Liner

One interesting display showed a sand exclusion liner made of sintered steel shot. The size of the shot determines the grain size which the liner will exclude. The liner is made in sections approximately six inches long and four inches in diameter with a sintered wall approximately one-half inch in thickness. The ends of each section are tapered — male on one end, female on the other so that a long length of liner can be assembled and welded together. This permits gradation in sieve size along the length of the liner. Sufficient welding is done so that the resulting section is mechanically strong, but has a high permeability. Use of the sand exclusion liner in the field so far has been limited. In the fields visited later, sand problems were being handled by plastic injection and consolidation.

"As part of its program to make all sources of information available to personnel in the oil, gas, and petrochemical industries, the USSR will begin to publish a complete translated monthly edition of The Petroleum Engineer in 1961. An annual subscription will cost 21 rubles (new rate), or by separate issue — 1 ruble, 75 kop."

"Read and Subscribe to the Translated Version of the Petroleum Engineer — the Universal Petroleum Journal of the US"

Fig. 6. Advertisement Soliciting Subscriptions to Translated Version of US Technical Journal

Photo No. 4. Display of Oil Field Equipment at the All-Union Permanent Exhibition of Science and Industry in Moscow.

b. Flat Rolled Pipeline

The pipe is manufactured at a rolling mill where two strips of steel approximately 3/16th inch in thickness and 14 inches in width are welded at each edge over an interval of approximately an inch. Continuous strips up to 2800 feet in length are wound on large diameter spools. The welds are automatically inspected by X-ray; the ends of the strip are welded shut. Near each end pressure fittings are provided for injecting air or water. A spool of this welded double strip is compact and occupies little shipping space as compared to 2800 feet of 8-inch pipe.

At location, one end of the strip is anchored, an axle is placed through the spool center, and it is unrolled by tractor along the path desired. Air or water or other fluid is pumped into the strip, expanding it into a circular cross-section. The result is an eight-inch diameter pipe, having two external one-inch flanges along each side. The technique is novel and offers advantages. Not only is it easier to ship, but installation of the pipeline is less time consuming and requires less labor than moving and joining short sections of pipe to form a pipeline. The delegation saw none of this pipe in use at the places visited later, but the exhibit had photographs of field installations.

c. Semi-Prefabricated Tanks

This development is directed toward economy in shipping and ease of installation. The bottom of the assembly consists of two semi-circular pieces of welded steel plate rolled onto a spindle. The sides of the tank, again of welded steel plate, are rolled onto a second spindle. The top is shipped in pie-shaped wedges of steel plate. Steel bracing is also supplied. At the site, a circular cement base is poured. On this, the semi-circular

Photo No. 5. Use of Semi-Prefabricated Storage Tanks for Construction of Facilities at the Stalingrad Refinery.

bottom sections are unrolled and welded together along the central diameter. Next, a pipe is installed vertically and fitted with umbrella-like bracing for supporting the top. The spindle carrying the side of the tank is erected at one edge and a tractor unrolls it around the periphery. It is then welded to the bottom sheet, to the vertical bracing and along the common seam. The cone-shaped roof is installed by welding the pie-shaped segments in place. The delegation did not see any of these tanks in the places visited in the fields, but was told that they were being used and were considered beyond the experimental stage.

d. Automatic Drilling Rig

The delegation saw in the petroleum exhibit an accurately scaled model of a completely automatic drilling rig which picked drill pipe out of a rack, coupled it to the joint in the hole, and proceeded to drill with automatically controlled weight on the bit. It was indicated that this equipment is not in routine use but that full scale equipment has been made and is on trial.

During later visits to oil fields, the delegation observed automatic slips and power breakout tongs like those in the exhibit in use on drilling rigs in widely separated parts of the country. At one well we saw on the ground the equipment to replace the derrick man. It had been used before but was not then installed on the rig. The engineer said plans were to continue experimenting. The slips and breakout tongs are obviously in routine manufacture and appear to work satisfactorily. At one rig, a set was down for repairs; apparently its construction is simple enough that repair can be carried out on the rig floor.

e. Electro-Drill
In the exhibit in the petroleum building, an electric drill is displayed, full scale with cut-away sections to show the details of its construction. Also, the cables and fittings for transmitting power to the drill pipe are exhibited. The drill itself is 12 meters long and 20 centimeters in diameter. It operates at 680 rpm, uses three-phase power at 1650 volts, and draws 150 amperes. Power consumed is 250 kilowatts. The swivel is attached to a commutator to supply the electric power to the drill through sections of electric cable mounted in each joint of drill pipe. The cable is coaxial, three-conductor, and each section is centrally held in its joint by plastic spiders. The female cable connector does not quite reach the end of the joint. The male connector extends past the tool joint threads, but is protected by a steel sleeve. As the new joint is rotated to make up to the pipe in the hole, the centered coaxial cable rotates and makes up in the connector. At New Karadag, on the Caspian Sea, where the equipment was observed in operation, a 12-meter drill collar was being used, and a weight of 14 tons was carried on the bit. Bit weight is automatically controlled. It was indicated at New Karadag that at shallow depths the electric drill was getting 700 meters per bit; at 2,100 meters, 30 meters per bit; at 3,000 meters, 10 to 15 meters per bit.

f. Offshore Rigs
There were two scale models of offshore drilling rigs at the exhibit; both types reportedly in use. These had mud sleeves as against piping and mud pits behind the pipe racks instead of using the under deck. The large rig appeared to have a number of features similar to Le Tourneau or De Long equipment. No new concepts were evident.

g. Bits
Tricone and four cone bits of various sizes were on display but no large diamond bits. Small diamond bits were seen in the geological exhibits later.

h. Logging Equipment
A variety of subsurface logging equipment was on display, single and multiple electrode E log assemblies, caliper logs, dip meter, well surveying tools and a down hole camera using 35 millimeter film. The engineers seemed quite proud of this. It is used especially in connection with hydrofracing to determine the location and patterns of fractures. Radioactivity logging devices were not pointed out, but the delegation was informed that these were in common use.

i. Geophysical Equipment
In the geological building at the exhibition some examples of geophysical prospecting equipment and well logging tools were on display. There were examples of ground and airborne magnetic equipment, resistivity, and electromagnetic inductance equipment, gravity meters, apparently using fused quartz systems, similar to meters made in the US, and several groups of seismic instruments. A large console for offshore seismic work appeared to consist of 60 amplifier channels each with high and low cut filters and

auxiliary controls. A conventional portable seismic system, having 24 channels, was packaged in four units, two for the amplifiers, one for the camera, and another for the sound powered telephone. No tape recording equipment was on display, but there was a magnetic playback console consisting of a 20 centimeter drum with a fixed magnetic coating coaxial with a second drum about 75 centimeters in diameter. The second drum carried a paper strip on the order of 30 centimeters in width on which a one-at-a-time pen recorder operated. Trace shifting was obviously possible and, probably, correction for geometric spreading.

2. Institute for Design of Oil Refineries — Giproneftezavod

The delegation met with the following:

Sorokin, Nikolai Ivanovitch	— Director
Yevstafiyev, Vseveled Vladzimirovich	— Chief, Process Design Department
Shteingol'ts, Izrail Vosipovich	— Assistant Chief, Process Design Department
Baskakov, Andres Alexandrovich	— Assistant Chief Engineer
Narsessov, Lazar Grigorivitch	— Assistant Chief, Technical Department
Makarov, Sergei K.	— Chief Engineer
Shripnik, Nelly	— Interpreter

This institute does process design for oil refineries but excluding power plants, water works and other, similar structures. The Institute has its main offices in Moscow with branches in Baku, Rostov, Kuybyshev, Gorkiy, and Omsk. Branch offices are directly under Moscow but are free to communicate across to assure liaison. Giproneft' also does design work for modification of existing plants unless the changes are minor.

The institute employs 2,000 people. Six hundred of these are in Moscow; two hundred to three hundred in each branch office. Half of the personnel are technical, 30 percent are semi-technical and 20 percent are draftsmen and service employees. This does not include employees in the Baku or Groznyy regions which are relatively autonomous.

The group designs plants for crudes which come largely from the Urals-Volga region. This region accounts for about 70 percent of USSR production. The Urals-Volga region has three basic types of crude:

Sulfur by percent weight		Percent of USSR Production	
		1952	1959
Type 1	Less than 0.5	na	18.0
Type 2	0.5 to 2	32.5	62.0
Type 3	2 to 4.2	na	19.5

Specific gravity ranges from 0.8 to 0.9.

Three general types of refining are in use:

I. Complete processing for crudes having a sulfur content up to 2 percent. This type of refinery has: atmospheric and vacuum primary distillation; thermal cracking; catalytic cracking; narrow cut fractionation of some catalytic products; catalytic reforming; lube oil refining (deasphalting and phenol treating); asphalt production. A full range of products are produced, including motor gasoline, jet and diesel fuels, a full viscosity range of lubes, wax, and, at some plants, asphalts.

II. Full-range fuel processing — for crudes having less than 2 percent sulfur. Processing follows same pattern as I without lube and asphalt steps.

III. Heavy fuel processing — for crudes having 2 percent to 5 percent sulfur. Atmospheric distillation only, with some visbreaking of the residuum. Produces gasolines, kerosines, diesel and residual fuel. When fuel for power plants is the prime objective, this type refinery may simply take off a light cut.

It was stated that use of residual fuels was being encouraged as a replacement for coal or other less economical fuels. The Soviet petroleum product balance is changing very rapidly to a greater demand for middle distillates and residual, but production of sufficient quantities of middle distillates remains a problem. Because refinery operations stress kerosine and diesel production, thermal and catalytic cracking processes will be developed extensively. In general, not much attention is given to secondary processing, such as hydrofining to remove sulfur — even for jet fuel, although a few such units have been installed. Petroleum coke, not an important fuel, is made for use in electrodes. Because of the high sulfur content the coke is poor quality but is considered usable. In new refineries catalytic cracking represents 18 to 25 percent of the refinery crude charge, the exact figure depending on local conditions.

It was said that regional needs dictate the product ratios. Gosplan enters to decide whether to build a refinery near production, or to transport crude to another region for refining.

A standard refinery may have a 6 million ton annual capacity and could consist of three 2 million ton or two 3 million ton primary distillation units, or it may have a single 6 million ton unit. Such a plant would employ 1,500 to 1,800 people for the refining and personnel services such as housing and transportation.

Representatives of this institute stated they could build a 1.5 million ton per year atmospheric and vacuum unit in nine months which would compare favorably with construction schedules in the US.

Pool gasoline quality is to be raised to 75 octane Motor Method Clear by 1963 and to 82 by 1965. Straight run gasolines now average 50 to 58 octane Motor Method. The octane rating may be as low as 47 occasionally or as high as 72. It was said that three cc of tetraethyl lead per gallon will raise the 50 to 60 octane to 82; one cc will do the same for the 75 octane.

The Soviet refineries use a urea (carbamide) process for dewaxing diesel oils.

The statement was made that they have platformers similar to U.O.P.

This group does no research. Refinery research is carried out in seven areas, five within Moscow and two elsewhere. Total personnel involved is 2,500 of whom 200 are Ph.D's or candidates and 700 are engineers. The research groups operate 60 pilot units and several integrated pilot plants.

3. All-Union Scientific and Research Institute on Crude Oil — VNIINeft'

At the institute the delegation met with the following:

Krylov, A. P.   — Director, Corresponding Member
                                   of the Academy of Sciences
Tereshchenko, A. M.   — Chief Engineer and Asst. Director

Maksimov, M. I.   — Chief of Development Department
Petrovskaya, A. N.   — Chief of Correlation Department
Shipova, V. V.   — Translator, Engineer
Virnovskiy, A. S.   — Assistant Director of Research
Maksimovich, G. K.   — Chief Specialist on Oil Production,
                                 Gosekonomsovet

Scope and Size

The institute is dedicated to research on long and intermediate range production problems relating to recovery and productivity. It is not interested in sulphur, salt, water emulsions, etc. The total staff in Moscow is 700, with women accounting for about 50 percent. In all there are about 400 scientific and engineering personnel. Two branches are maintained — one in the Turkmen republic and another in Krasnodar Kray. The institute occasionally undertakes important short-range projects in major oil fields.

Supporting Activity

Basic research in other sciences needed for production research is carried out in such separate institutes as the Institute for Physics Research, the Institute for Chemical Research and the Institute for Geological Research. Fundamental research in science and engineering is also carried out at various universities. In addition, the separate trusts which are responsible for drilling, well logging, cementing and hydrofracing do some development research which must overlap into or support the applied production research done at the institute. The delegation saw evidence for this supporting work in the All-Union Permanent Exhibition of Science and Industry and in the field in the automated producing and drilling equipment and the turbo and electro-drills.

Programming and Communication

The program is set up by annual and interim meetings of research and operating personnel. The resulting program is described as both field and self-generated. Final responsibility lies with the research organization except where it is modified by higher authority. The institute recognizes the problems in communicating with the operating groups, all of which are geographically remote from its laboratory. These difficulties cover both communications regarding the research program and acceptance of research results by operating groups. The institute has the authority to take its ideas into the field for proper testing and, in fact, has the responsibility of testing developments until it is convinced they are ready for application.

Laboratory Organization

The laboratory is broken down into several divisions believed to be as follows:

I. Geology Department
    1. Development Geology — Geological studies of reservoirs to determine size, shape, water level, permeability variations, etc.
    2. Exploitation Geophysics (Petro-physics) — Development and use of various logging methods and interpretation of logging data for parameters of interest in exploitation, such as porosity and saturation.
    3. Reservoir Engineering — Prediction of reservoir behavior under different production practices.

II. Physics and Hydrodynamics Department
1. Flow in porous media and fluid displacement problems. Related physics problems are solved here for the other departments in the laboratory. Makes isotopic tracer studies in oil fields.
2. Computing Section — Computing services for the rest of the laboratory are centered here.

III. Oil Field Development Department
1. Recovery — Studies recovery problems as functions of well spacing, pressure maintenance, etc. Works on instrumentation for bottomhole pressure measurements.
2. Analog Models — Uses electrical analog models for detailed oil field studies.

IV. Production Engineering Department
1. Well stimulation, hydrofracing, water treatment for injection, automation and control.

V. Petroleum Economics
1. Planning and organization with respect to manpower, equipment, and techniques for optimum results.

VI. Services Department
1. Information services, editing, and publishing technical reports.
2. Shops — fabrication of specialized research equipment.
3. Housekeeping.

Specific Projects

The delegation was shown a number of individual laboratories where there was an opportunity to see and briefly discuss such items as:

1. An electric analog computer for reservoir study, containing 20,000 meshes. The operation of the analog for a particular reservoir is made in steps, each usually representing three or four months so that parameters can be changed to increase modeling accuracy. Such analog computers are particularly useful to the Soviet Union because of their policy of water injection. Apparently, quite detailed studies are made of the reservoir before the final production pattern is established. An attempt is made to be as realistic and detailed as possible with respect to geology, geometry, the porosity and permeability of each reservoir of consequence.

2. A flow experiment, using a series of cylindrical, porous cores of increasing diameter to approximate radial flow. This was being done to simulate combinations of water-drive with other stimulation methods under reservoir conditions.

A model consisting of a nest of concentric brass screens presumably for bottom-water coning experiments. This could be called a visual model of radial flow. The scheme was not entirely clear. It is possible they were using capacitance measurements to locate the interface between oil and water and that the brass screens simulated a porous median.

4. A vertical slab model for studying the effect of rates of injection and withdrawal. In order to scale the capillary forces the dimensions of this model are quite large and to accommodate the necessary length in a small room, it has been folded back on itself several times. The effective length is in this way 60 to 80 feet.

5. Panels designed for central control of one to two hundred wells.
6. Equipment for measuring various rock and fluid parameters useful in production and engineering.

General Information

Discussion and comments at various points during the tour of the laboratory developed the following information: the goal with respect to a reservoir is to extract the maximum with due consideration to cost and time. Their aim is for a 25-year life. However, it was admitted that such considerations as refinery demand had a large say in actual rates of production.

Sixty-three percent of the production in the USSR currently comes from fields being water flooded. Injection in new discoveries is begun early in the field life. Peripheral injection is adequate for small fields. For large ones, or for fields with low permeability, interspaced injection is used as well as peripheral. Originally pressure maintenance was aimed at keeping the initial reservoir pressure; now higher pressures are being tried in an effort to produce more oil through fewer wells.

At present only shallow reservoirs with good permeability, high porosity and low viscosity are exploited. Permeabilities are said to range from 200 to 500 millidarcies and viscosities from 3 to 5 centipoises. Ninety-seven percent of the USSR production is from sandstone reservoirs. Interest was expressed in experience and case histories of water floods in limestone reservoirs. Although there is little limestone production in the USSR at present, more is anticipated in the future. A USSR recovery of 60 percent of the oil in place is the current estimate but many fields will go as high as 80 percent.

When a discovery is made, stepout wells are drilled to define the extent of the reservoir, to locate the oil-water contact and the gas-oil contact. On the basis of this and a study of the reservoir characteristics the pattern for the oil and injection well system is laid out. It should be mentioned that these step-out wells are listed as exploratory in Soviet statistics and, therefore, make a direct comparison of discovery ratios with those in the western world meaningless.

The USSR has a few high viscosity fields in which bottom hole heaters are used. Where massive sands are encountered, for example 300 feet or more, as many as ten drain holes may be drilled into the reservoir from each well to increase productivity. Only a little gas injection is being used for pressure maintenance. A few experiments are being carried out with miscible floods.

In logging operations the Soviet engineers use electrical logs, radioactive logs and a bottom hole camera for studying wall faces in their injection well. They do not appear to have an acoustic log and were not familiar with its use in our country, possibly because they do so little work in limestone. It was indicated that hydrofracing was used primarily for improving injectivity of water wells rather than for increasing the productivity of production wells.

The average oil well production in the USSR was said to be 5,650 tons per year*. In the Urals-Volga region the average production is 17,000 tons

---

*If true, this average production per well would indicate a total of only 26,200 active oil wells in the USSR. For derivation of probably a more accurate figure, see page 75.

per year and in the Baku region 3,000 tons per year. Wells in a few Soviet fields have reached 45,000 to 50,000 tons per year.

The work of the economic department was said to be concerned with the optimum use of technique, equipment and manpower but aside from the general remarks on optimum field life it was not possible to determine what constituted the optimum. Capital investments such as wells were said to be amortized over fixed periods of time. The impression was given that the concept of present worth was not employed.

This institute publishes all levels of technical literature dealing with oil production. There are three magazines for different technical levels, and bulletins and books are published as material is released.

Miscellaneous

In addition to the experimental fluid flow it was indicated that theoretical studies of multiphase flow were being conducted. No mention was made here or elsewhere of a digital computer. Probably such equipment would be available in one of the more basic institutes. No electric calculators of any kind were observed at this laboratory, and only one small, hand-cranked mechanical model. Every desk, however, contained an abacus.

At least half the personnel were women and a considerable number of these were classified as researchers. The quarters were all quite crowded and the physical plant generally shabby. The experimental equipment in use was spartan by US standards, but presumably adequate for the straightforward problems in hand.

4. Ufa Scientific and Research Institute on Crude Oil and Natural Gas — UfNIING

Bayrak, K.A.	— Director
Babalyan, G.A.	— Assistant Director for Research
Vissarionova, A.Ya.	— Assistant Director for Geology
Permyakov, I.G.	— Chief, Development Department
Sattarov, M.M.	— Chief, Development Laboratory
Glezer, D.Kh.	— Chief, Laboratory for Methods of Extraction
Mavlyutov, M.Z.	— Chief, Oil Preparation Laboratory
Kravchenko, I.I.	— Chief, Laboratory for Surface Tension Reducing Agents
Latypov, E.K.	— Chief, Drilling Department
Genkin, I.B.	— Chief, Economics Department
Sukhankin, Ye.I.	— Chief Laboratory for Oil in situ Research
Markhasin, I.L.	— Chief, Laboratory for Reservoir Physics
Lobkov, A.M.	— Chief, Gas Section
Korokova, R.G.	— Translator

Scope and Size

This institute is primarily interested in production research. It had the following departments: Geology, Drilling, Development, Production, Gas and Economics. These categories are of primary interest to the economic region in which the institute is located. Similar institutes exist in each of the economic regions where oil is produced.

The total staff consists of 600 people, 420 of whom are called engineers and scientific research personnel. About one-third of the department heads are women and approximately two-thirds of the laboratory technicians are

Photo No. 6. The Ufa Scientific and Research Institute on Crude Oil and Natural Gas.

women. Present plans are for the institute staff to be increased to 800 in the near future which will require an addition to their research building and facilities. The building and its facilities were better built and better maintained than the All-Union research establishment visited in Moscow. The institute has a good-sized auditorium for staff meetings and seminars. The auditorium is also used for technical meetings for the exchange of ideas between research personnel and operating personnel. In 1959, for instance, an all-union research conference on the use of surfactants was held in the auditorium.

The following individual laboratories were visited:

1. Laboratory for spectral analysis — Items seen here were:

a. A spectrometer for 2,400 to 4,000 angstrom range used for analyzing sedimentary rocks for trace metals. It was being used specifically for correlating Devonian fossil fragments on the basis of different vanadium, nickel, and iron content.

b. A spectrometer for the 4,000 to 9,000 angstrom range.

c. A new differential thermal analysis apparatus used for clay correlations. It had an automatic 15 minute cycle and was self-recording.

2. Geochemical Laboratory — Attention here is on the chemistry of Devonian and Carboniferous rocks and fluids with attention to extraction. Important parameters are specific gravity, viscosity, chemical fractionation, percentages of hydrogen sulphide, sulphur, paraffin, asphaltines and tars. It was stated that Bashkirian crude in general runs:

2 to 3.5 percent sulphur
2 to 4 percent paraffin
3 to 5 percent asphaltines
20 percent gasoline
20 percent kerosine
60 percent residual fuel oil (mazut).

Specific gravity of the crude is from .85 to .86; specific gravity of the mazut .903 to .908. Production from older horizons is said to be lighter in gravity and there is some indication that this crude has a lower sulphur content.

This group is quite interested in determining the variations in composition of oils with respect to the age and the geographic distribution of rocks in which they occur.

Natural Gasoline Laboratory

This installation was completed about 18 months prior to our visit, following an important gas-condensate discovery in the area. The group is concerned with production gas analyses and the stabilization of gas-condensate. It is involved in process design for improved absorption units and stabilization units. In the case of the discovery mentioned, propane content is 600 cubic centimeters per cubic meter, about half of which is currently extracted. The gas contains 7 to 10 percent nitrogen and a varying quantity of hydrogen sulphide. At present, there are no facilities for extracting hydrogen sulphide from the casinghead gas.

Laboratory for Utilization of Casinghead Gas

This unit, set up in 1958, is concerned with the quantity and quality of casinghead gases and with separator problems. Hydrate formation occurs with some condensate production. Liquid condensation in pipelines is another problem. The delegation was told that equipment for analyzing for rare gases was in the process of being checked out, but none was seen.

PVT Laboratory

Equipment was in operation here for studying the pressure-volume-temperature properties of reservoir fluids for research purposes and for routine service to the various oil fields. Equipment was available for preparing reconstituted liquid and gas samples from the field. Work was also being done on material from bottom hole samplers.

The function of this group is to provide numbers used by other departments for hydrodynamic studies, the computation of decline curves and reservoir calculations.

Laboratory for Paraffin Research

In this laboratory both physical and chemical factors influencing paraffin deposition are studied with the view of developing more effective methods of preventing deposition both down the hole and in the producing tubular strings. A flying scrubber developed in this laboratory is in field use; an electrical polarizing method was tried, but did not work. The group is experimenting with lacquers and paints for inside coating of production strings.

Laboratory for Drilling Muds

Primary interest is in muds suitable for deep holes and temperatures up to 150° centigrade useful for drilling, but which will not damage potential reservoirs. High temperatures were said to be no problem, 100° centigrade being the maximum measured in their deepest hole in Bashkiria. Their deepest hole is presently drilling at 3,670 meters, where low water loss muds were being used.

Deep holes in the USSR are those below 4,500 meters. In the Bashkira ASSR, there has been no real need to drill deep wells, because adequate reserves are present at depths above 2,000 meters. Now there is interest in exploration below those depths. In this deeper exploration, they have apparently encountered a problem similar to our "heaving shales" in the Gulf Coast. Normally, low water loss muds are used, but there have been some trials of oil base muds. It was indicated that in other areas oil emulsion muds as well as oil base muds were being used in a routine fashion. One of these areas is believed to be near Stalingrad.

Research work is in progress on the study of the rheology of high temperature muds in which surface tension reducing agents are incorporated to increase the productivity of producing formations. One of the problems is the foaming caused by surfactants introduced into drilling muds. This is particularly noticeable with turbodrills. Experiments with air drilling have been made, but in the Bashkir ASSR there are too many water bearing horizons to allow the methods to operate satisfactorily.

Laboratory for Well Stimulation

This group studies means for increasing the productivity of reservoirs and performance of injection wells. Acid washing has been in use for some time and use of surfactants has started. Hydrofracing is done with jelled oils and occasionally with jelled acids. Water treatment problems for maintaining high injectivity of water input wells are studied. The group also undertakes tests of injection wells for permeability. It was said that this institute did not work on perforating methods. A separate institute exists for this function.

Hydrodynamics Laboratory

At this laboratory an electrical analog for modeling reservoir hydrodynamics was exhibited. The unit has a 17 x 29 grid and can handle parameters for permeability, layer thickness and viscosity. Fluid velocity and pressure distribution can be determined for various rates of withdrawal, rates of injection and various well distribution patterns. This computer was much smaller than the one seen in Moscow and was operated in a continuous fashion rather than being pulsed. The primary purpose is to control water flood projects.

Theoretical work on the displacement of oil by water is being carried out in this part of the institute. Help on basic data and fundamental physics comes from the All-Union Institute in Moscow and from other research centers.

Core Laboratory

Routine measurements on cores are made here to determine the residual oil saturation, porosity and permeability. Flood pot tests were being carried out on cores at the time of our visit, particularly cores with large clay content to determine permeability to reservoir water and waters proposed for injection.

Experimental Fluid Flow Laboratory

This group undertakes fluid flow work. In one experiment, the total length of core was approximately one meter, made up of sections approximately 5 centimeters in length enclosed in a flanged rubber sleeve. This entire core had been assembled in a unit so that fluid pressure could be introduced into the space around the core at a pressure higher than the inside pressure so that no leakage could occur around the core edges. This was one arrangement for working on relative permeabilities between gas and oil and between water and oil under simulated in situ conditions. Other experiments were being done in a room held at a constant temperature of 24° C. No information was given on the kind of work performed here.

Paleo Laboratory
Here three micro-paleontologists were at work on correlations and environment problems.

Geological Museum
One fairly large room was dedicated to samples of geologically and economically interesting rocks and minerals from the Urals. Most of the rocks were igneous, but there were a few specimens of sedimentary rock from oil producing areas.

5. Stalingrad Scientific and Research Institute on Crude Oil and Natural Gas — SNIING

On arrival from Baku late in the afternoon the delegation met the following members of the Stalingrad Scientific-Research Institute on Crude Oil and Gas:

Korneyev, V.I.	— Director
Goryachev, A.A.	— Chief Engineer, Oil and Gas Administration
Somov, B.V.	— Chief Engineer, Stalingrad Sovnarkhoz
Razanov	— Chief Geologist and Assistant Director
Kotelnikov	— Chief of Production and Assistant Director
Zaridov	— Chief of Refining
Gaitov	— Expert on drilling; member of Stalingrad Sovnarkhoz
Senyagovskiy	— Chief, Production Technology
Volodin	— Refining expert, member of Stalingrad Sovnarkhoz

The laboratories of this institute were not visited but were described as similar to those at Ufa but newer. This institute has a staff of 650 in a relatively new building but the group is expected to grow to 800 by the end of 1961, at which time a new building will be required. About half the technical staff are women. There are departments of geology, exploration geophysics, production, drilling and refining. From the geological group it was learned that they were doing research on electrical prospecting methods and were very much interested in the mechanism of salt dome growth and the relation of growth to accumulation. Although there is a refining section in the Institute it was claimed that there is no refinery in Stalingrad. This claim is not supported by current Soviet literature, which has publicized the completion of a refinery at Stalingrad in 1957. This refinery reportedly replaced one which had blown up before it had even been placed on stream. It was indicated that one was to be constructed in the fairly near future which might include petro-chemicals. It appeared that their studies here included petro-chemical synthesis.

The delegation inquired as to how a scientific unit of this type was set up. We were told that jobs were advertised in local papers and in trade journals having all-union circulation. Applications were received and their qualifications reviewed by a committee specifically set up for this purpose consisting of department heads of the institute, experts in phases of the institute work and members of the sovnarkoz. Applicants were narrowed down on the basis of this committee's appraisal. When applicants for a particular job were narrowed to two or three, personal preference by the administration might then be allowed. This system of advertising is required even though a man is locally available and qualified for promotion to a vacancy. We were also told that all scientific jobs are advertised every five years and the incumbent must reapply for his own job in competition with any others who apply. This does not appear to apply to non-research engineers in refineries and oil fields.

Photo No. 7. A General View of the Unit for Selective Refining of Lube Oils at the Stalingrad Refinery.

6. Stalingrad Sovnarkoz

Whereas Gosplan is responsible for short and intermediate range planning for the USSR as a whole, the sovnarkoz or regional economic council, of which there are 105 in the USSR, carries out these general plans and makes specific plans for all industry within its territory.* Having had a meeting with Gosplan in Moscow the delegation was anxious to have a discussion with one of the councils. On August 20 the delegation met with the following members of the petroleum section of the Stalingrad Sovnarkoz:

Mazanov	— Chief, Oil and Gas Section
Goryachev	— Chief Engineer
Gabrilyan, A.G.	— Chief Geologist
Fershter	— Chief Specialist, Drilling
Krasnow, A.S.	— Director, Geophysical Office
Kratz	— Chief Bookkeeper
Grotengeim	— Chief Economist

Within the petroleum section are departments of geology, drilling, production, reservoir engineering, machine power, transportation, construction, accounting, food supply and others. The idea seems to be to make the oil business as self-sufficient as possible with respect to other industries.

---

*For a more detailed discussion of the role of the sovnarkoz in national planning, see page 14.

In reply to a question as to where funds were derived for exploration, development or building refineries, the answer was that all the funds came from Gosplan. When asked about funds for, say, an acceleration in exploration which appeared advantageous on the local scene, it was stated that a recommendation could be made to Gosplan. If Gosplan concurred, it would authorize the expenditure and would issue permits for the needed personnel.

Photo No. 8. Rectification Columns of the Unit for Selective Refining of Lube Oils at the Stalingrad Refinery.

It was remarked that dealing with the trade unions posed a considerable problem. The unions have funds at their disposal and have definite rules regarding pay scales, hours worked, upgrading, time off with pay for education, for vacation, illness and rest cures. The unions share in industry bonuses and also receive a percentage of the total money spent on wage and salary. They spend these funds on kindergartens, rest homes (vacation camps), education for adults, promoting sports, etc. It is possible the labor discussion was brought up as an excuse to list the things being done for labor.

In response to a question as to the effect on wages of the success or failure of an enterprise, we were told that that had nothing to do with the wages paid. Given categories are paid the same regardless of short-term economics. However, if an enterprise exceeds its quota, it may receive a bonus. Thirty percent of this goes to the "directors" fund. Based on agreements with the trade unions this is spent on improving schools, the plant, rest homes, building palaces of culture, etc.

In discussing production rates, it appeared that the Soviet Union might produce gas reserves as rapidly in some cases as twenty percent a year in the current stage of planning. Oil reserves are extracted at rates between four and six percent with preference for the former. From this and current production figures, the Sovnarkoz agreed that the Soviet reserves would be in the neighborhood of three billion tons.

At this meeting we were shown a geologic section across the Stalingrad region in a WNW direction. The section was compared structurally by the Soviet geologists to the Gulf Coast, because it increased gradually from the west by expansion and addition for about two-thirds the distance, to a point where the basement lay below 3,400 meters, and then expanded very rapidly into the Caspian depression. The bulk of the expansion below the hinge took place in the Permian evaporites. At the hinge point the Carboniferous was about 1,500 meters thick, the Devonian close to 2,000. Silurian and Ordovician apparently have not been found in the region.

At present, concentration has been placed on the development of structures well up on the shelf, such as at Archeda and Zhirnovsk, where there is Carboniferous and Devonian production. The geologists are aware of the stratigraphic possibilities here and of the possibilities of the numerous salt domes lying in the deeper parts of the basin, but implied they were saving them until all of the simple structures had been explored. They are using the seismograph extensively in exploratory work and have covered the entire region by gravity meter. Other geophysical prospecting methods do not appear to have been used extensively. An experimental telluric survey was mentioned but the results were not discussed.

The statement was made that compared to other regions a relatively large number of exploratory tests here would be equivalent to our new field wildcats. The implication was that this area is in an early stage of the exploration cycle.

7. State Scientific and Technical Committee — GNTK

The delegation had two meetings in Moscow with the State Scientific and Technical Committee, our official hosts while we were in the Soviet Union. This committee was abolished in early April 1961 and replaced by a new State Committee for Coordinating Scientific Research. This move apparently reflected a desire to eliminate duplication in the research effort of the USSR. Previously, research came under the jurisdiction of two bodies — the Academy of Sciences and the State Scientific and Technical Committee. The proper function of the Academy of Sciences had been questioned for some time.

The State Scientific and Technical Committee, which was attached to the Council of Ministers, USSR, had as its function the recommendation of new techniques and technology to the field and, in addition, followed through on these recommendations to see that they are accorded the proper attention. Each republic in the USSR had such a committee.

The purpose of the first session with the GNTK was to discuss the itinerary of the US delegation in its final form. Some negotiation was required, particularly with reference to the visit to the Novo-Kuybyshev refinery. The delegation asked for permission to visit an offshore oil field in the Caspian Sea, specifically Neftyanyye Kamni. The request was granted, if in return the Soviet oil delegation to the US would be allowed to visit one of our offshore operations.

The purpose of the second session with this committee, held at the close of the tour, was to present a brief report on the findings and impressions of the delegation. The report was presented by W.W. Keller, chairman of the delegation, who noted that the delegation had spent 46 hours in refineries and oil fields plus 20 hours in discussions with the various institutes.

The report stated our favorable impression of the Soviet oil man. It was obvious that the USSR was making rapid strides along cultural and educational lines. Production and development research was good though done with a minimum of equipment. The delegation was favorably impressed by evidence of drilling and production automation and, in particular, by the turbo and the bottom hole, electric drill.

Because of wide differences in type of product desired in the USSR and the US we found no specific ideas for improving our refinery processes. We were surprised not to see any catalytic reforming in view of the Soviet need for diesel fuel vs gasoline. Other impressions of the refineries were use of multiple units instead of single ones of large capacity, the sprawled out nature of the operations and the lack of safety items, fire and otherwise. We also noted the large labor force, both in production and refining.

We commended our hosts on their conservation practices as applied to production — especially on their water flooding operations.

We mentioned our favorable impression of the recognition given to individuals in the fields and plants.

In reply Mr. Notkin felt that the US delegation had obtained a good grasp of the situation in the places visited considering the shortness of our stay. He regretted the lack of opportunity to see some refining research which was taking care of many of the problems we had noted. The Leningrad Institute, he said, is working on catalytic reforming with the view toward large scale future use. It is, in fact, used at several refineries not visited but not in the improved state anticipated.

He agreed the USSR uses more labor than the US. This is in large part to provide a labor pool for projected rapid expandion. Extra labor is also required in part because some processes are not as fully automated as they will be.

The wide separation of units in refineries is being corrected in new plans.

He did not agree fully on our remarks on safety. Their record is good. Also, each plant has a full time fire brigade as against use of individual extinguishers by regular personnel. Regular personnel, however, are now being trained to fight fire.

On our complaints about the lack of information obtained from Gosplan, Mr. Notkin said we were informed in advance that we would get no replies on certain subjects.

Mr. Notkin stated that they could now satisfy home demand and had a surplus for export. Some items such as diesel fuels still were in short supply because of the relatively rapid rise in internal consumption. Because of this the USSR has a surplus of gasoline. This will be balanced in the near term by producing more gasoline consuming engines than in the past. Both home demand and export offer great possibilities.

Mr. Piercy asked what would happen if Soviet planning was faulty. For instance, would they dump through export if production shot out of balance by 50 million tons in any given year. Mr. Notkin said they could easily absorb that much internally. They would be glad to push ahead of coal faster than planned.* Two years ago all locomotives were coal burning, in five

---

*It appears doubtful that the goal of 600-612 million tons of coal by 1965 will be achieved. The 1961 plan for coal — 511 million tons — is less than 1960 actual production. It is probable that the desired increment in coal production during the period 1959-65 of about 110 million tons will not be achieved and that actual coal production by 1965 may not exceed 560 million tons.

years all will be electric or diesel except for small branch lines. No coal burning locomotives have been produced in 18 months. The number two fuel consumer, power stations, are easily switched from the poor Soviet coal to oil. In short, he did not think the fact the Soviets expected to exceed their Seven Year plan goals by 10 to 50 percent was going to create an oversupply.

At this point and on request Mr. Piercy gave a short outline of the future oil picture in the United States.

The following were present at both meetings:

Notkin, D.I.	— Chief, Division of Petroleum Industry, State Scientific-Economic Council (Gosekonomsovet)
Aleksenko, G.V.	— Vice Chairman
Gvishiani, D.M.	— Chief, Foreign Relations Division
Sorokin, N.I.	— Director, Institute for the Design of Oil Refineries (Giproneftezavod)
Gorbunov, Vladimir	— Interpreter, Institute of Information
Mal'kov, I.A.	— Chief Specialist, Oil Drilling
Basistov, A.A.	— Chief Specialist, Oil Refining
Polyakov, D.N.	— Chief, Anglo-Saxon Section
Maksimovich, G.K.	— Chief Specialist on Oil Production, State Scientific-Economic Council (Gosekonomsovet)
Putilin, B.G.	— Expert, Division of Foreign Relations
Shvarts, I.P.	— Interpreter, Protocol Department
Tikhomirov, Hori Borisovich	— Chief of Protocol

VIII. EXPLORATION

The delegation did not have an opportunity to observe exploration procedures in the Soviet oil industry. Therefore, an evaluation of this phase must be based on methods used to discover those fields which the delegation visited, a consideration of the dates of discovery, and, of course, discussions with production and research geologists whenever possible.

Of the fields which the delegation visited, only one — New Karadag — was discovered through the use of the seismograph, but the quality of this accomplishment was very high. The Tuymazy-Oktyabrsk field in the Urals-Volga and the Zhirnovsk field northwest of Stalingrad were found by surface geology. This evidence, coupled with the high level of Soviet geological literature and of the instrumentation on display at the All-Union Permanent Exhibition of Science and Industry in Moscow, lends strength to the belief that the Soviet exploratory capability is adequate for the tasks assigned to it.

About 11 million square kilometers of the Soviet land mass are suitable for the occurrence of petroleum, as illustrated by map no. 3. To explore this vast area calls for a significant effort in training, equipping and assigning geophysical field crews. In 1958 the USSR had 447 seismograph crews in the field, and the US only 422. In 1952, the peak year for the US, 660 crews were at work. By 1965, Soviet planners hope to have as many as 1,200 crews in the field. When it is remembered that these crews are not competing with each other, the figures become even more striking. In addition, more extensive use is being made of other geophysical and geochemical methods. The number of geophysical crews in use in the USSR, according to method of search, for selected years 1940-58 is shown in Table 14.

The next phase in the Soviet exploratory program is the drilling of

GEOLOGIC PROVINCES, SEDIMENTARY BASINS, AND PETROLEUM PRODUCING AREAS, U.S.S.R.

GEOLOGIC PROVINCES	SEDIMENTARY BASINS OR AREAS				PETROLEUM PRODUCING AREAS*		
	Name and geographic description	Approximate area	Approximate maximum thickness of sediments	Dominant geologic era	No.	Geographic name or area	Dominant production oil or gas
		1,000 sq. km.	km.				
CAUCASUS............ Includes Black Sea and the Middle and Southern part of the Caspian Sea.	Western Black Sea including Moldavian SSR.	60	4	Cenozoic.	......	....	
	Azov-Kuban'-Middle Caspian includes Sea of Azov and Kerch' Peninsula, eastward across the north Caucasus, Terek River basin, middle Caspian Sea, and the Krasnovodsk Area in Turkmen.	420	5	Cenozoic.	1	Kerch' Peninsula: minor prod.	Oil.
					2	Maikop-Krasnodar area..	Oil.
					3	Stavropol' area..........	Gas.
					4	Budennovsk area........	Oil.
					5	Groznyy-Makhachkala area.	Oil.
					6	Derbent area............	Gas.
	Eastern Black Sea including offshore area.	20	2	Cenozoic.	7	Poti area; minor prod....	Oil.
	Southern Caspian includes the Apsheron Peninsula at Baku and offshore areas of the southern Caspian; and the Kura River basin, and the Nebit-Dag area in Turkmen.	160	9	Cenozoic.	8	Upper Kura River valley.	Oil.
					9	Apsheron Peninsula......	Oil.
					10	Offshore area............	Oil.
					11	Lower Kura River valley.	Oil.
					12	Nebit-Dag area..........	Oil.
RUSSIAN PLATFORM........ Comprises all of the European U.S.S.R. lying north of the Caucasus and west of the Ural Mountains.	Western Ukraine-Baltic includes the sub-Carpathian area, the Brest basin, and the Baltic basin.	100	4	Cenozoic. Mesozoic. Paleozoic.	13	Borislav area............	Oil.
					14	Stryy area..............	Gas.
					15	Stanislav area..........	Oil.
	Dnepr-Don	140	4	Mesozoic.	16	Romny area, minor prod.	Oil.
					17	Shebilinskiy area........	Gas.
					18	Kharkov area............	Gas.
	Moscow includes adjacent areas.	840	3	Paleozoic.	......	....	
	Pechora.................	200	3	Paleozoic.	19	Ukhta area..............	Oil.
					20	Izhma area..............	Gas.
	Ural-Volga..............	540	5	Paleozoic.	21	Perm' area..............	Oil.
					22	Ishimbay-Ufa area.......	Oil.
					23	Eastern Tatar ASSR.....	Oil.
					24	Western Bashkir ASSR...	Oil.
					25	Kuybyshev area..........	Oil.
					26	Saratov area............	Gas.
					27	Stalingrad area..........	Gas.
	Emba also called northern Caspian or pre-Caspian basin.	560	6	Mesozoic.	28	Gur'yev area............	Oil.
					29	Shubar-Kuduk..........	Oil.
CENTRAL ASIA............. Also referred to as the Turan Plain. (Turanskaya Nizmennost')	Ustyurt.................	340	4	Cenozoic.	......	....	
	Turgoisk................	220	3	Cenozoic.	......	....	
	Kyzyl-Kum..............	320	4	Cenozoic.	......	....	
	Karakumy includes the valley of the Amu Dar'ya along the Afghanistan border.	440	5	....	30	Bukhara area............	Gas.
					31	Termez area.............	Oil.
	Chu....................	140	4	Paleozoic.	......	....	
	Fergana................	40	6	Cenozoic.	32	Kim area...............	Oil.
					33	Andizhan area...........	Oil.
WESTERN SIBERIAN PLAIN.... The area between the Urals and the Yenisey River.	Ob'-Taz................	760	6	Mesozoic.	34	Berezovo area...........	Gas.
	Irtysh..................	1,000	6	Mesozoic.	......	....	
	Yenisey.................	350	5	Mesozoic.	......	....	
CENTRAL SIBERIA........... All of the area east of the Yenisey River, to the U.S.S.R. Far East.	Taymyr.................	300	3	Mesozoic.	......	....	
	Khatanga...............	140	3	Mesozoic.	35	Nordvik area; minor prod.	Oil.
	Vilyuy.................	400	4	Mesozoic.	36	Vilyuy area; discovery only.	Gas.
	Angara.................	35	3	Mesozoic.	......	....	
	Aginsk.................	50	2	Mesozoic.	......	....	
	Zeya...................	75	2	Mesozoic.	......	....	
	Amur...................	50	2	Mesozoic.	......	....	
U.S.S.R. FAR EAST........ Comprises the maritime provinces bordering on the Sea of Japan, Sea of Okhotsk, and the Bering Sea.	Sakhalin including offshore.	20	3	Cenozoic.	37	Okha-Ekhabi area.......	Oil.
	Kamchatka including offshore.	70	3	Cenozoic.	38	Katangli area...........	Oil.
	Penzhino...............	20	2	Mesozoic.	......	....	
	Anadyr.................	60	2	Mesozoic.	......	....	
	Total area of 30 basins............	7,870					
	Average maximum thickness......	....	4.5				

* Denotes areas within which proved petroleum deposits occur.

Table 14

Geophysical Field Crews in the USSR, According to Method of Search
Selected Years, 1940-58

Method	1940	1946	1950	1955*	1956*	1957	1958
Seismic	18	24	118	250	321	350	447
Electric	31	37	88	68	91	90	125
Gravimetric	21	30	52	107	145	145	188
Magnetic	16	16	21	4	13	25	16
Airborne magnetometer	0	0	0	6	6	0	9
Total	86	107	279	435	576	610	785
Supporting	43	85	292	330	393	370	na
Grand Total	129	192	571	675	969	980	na

*Excluding Azerbaydzhan SSSR.

structural and prospecting holes. Through the drilling of structural holes, the USSR seeks information on the geological structure of deep-lying strata. This drilling also provides a basis for the drilling of prospecting wells which, in turn, determine the presence or absence of crude oil or natural gas.

The volume of structural-prospecting drilling in the USSR has been equivalent in recent years to about 80 percent of the volume of exploratory drilling. In 1959, about 3.5 million meters were drilled in the structural-prospecting program. During the Seven Year Plan, for every meter of exploratory hole drilled, there has been planned 0.78 meters of structural-prospecting drilling. The annual volume of structural-prospecting drilling is to reach to about 6 million meters by 1965. Concomitantly, the average depth of structural-prospecting holes is to increase from 502 meters in 1958 to 935 meters in 1965. As a part of this growth, the share of structural wells with depths up to 500 meters is to decline from 60 percent to 18 percent, and the share of wells with depths from 500 meters to 1,200 meters must increase from 31 percent to 46 percent.

It is probable that the USSR stands today where the US stood in 1930 in the extent of the exploration of its oil lands. But the USSR has at its disposal the latest geological, geophysical, logging and drilling techniques. This advantage is appreciated; the geologists with whom the delegation met stated that they were not interested in looking for "problem" production such as around salt domes, carbonates, or in stratigraphic traps. These areas will be by-passed at present. The current tendency is to concentrate on the search for structural traps, largely because the capability of search for stratigraphic traps still is low. Nevertheless, it is not difficult to forecast continued major discoveries on the part of Soviet geologists.

IX. EXPLORATORY AND DEVELOPMENT DRILLING

A. General

It is probable that the technical know-how, equipment quality and equipment quantity will not present serious blocks to the USSR in the developing and producing of crude oil. Yet some of the Soviet oil drilling techniques are an enigma in themselves. Drilling rigs show a shortage of steel; wooden walkways are used as are wooden or earth mud pits. On the other hand, derricks with crown blocks, traveling blocks and the like lie scattered over most of their fields. The layout of the derricks and auxiliary equipment seems awkward to the point that it must slow down the setting up or tearing down of a rig. It is estimated that it probably would take from two to three times longer for Soviet crews to set up than the general US standard.

The much-publicized turbodrill and the lesser-known electrodrill appear to be serviceable pieces of equipment. Currently the turbodrill accounts for about 85 percent of all exploratory and development drilling, the electrodrill for only 2 percent, and rotary and cable-tool for the remainder. Considerable praise has been given to the electrodrill and in selected tests the performance of this tool exceeds that of the turbodrill, particularly in commercial speed (meters per rig-month). In addition, the cost per meter drilled by the electrodrill has been lower than costs of drilling by the turbodrill under similar conditions.

Nevertheless, the problem of reduced bit life is evident for both of these drilling tools. In tertiary clastics, penetration per bit was reported to be 600 meters at shallow depths, 45 meters per bit between depths of 1,200 and 1,500 meters, and only 8 meters per bit below 3,000 meters. In the cherty Paleozoic carbonates of the Urals-Volga region, 25 meters per bit for depths on the order of 1,500 meters was given as standard performance. Drilling crews use water down to about 600 meters. The delegation was puzzled by the numerous instances of discarded bits whose cutting edges were only slightly worn. It was inferred that they were discarded because of bearing failure. The delegation was told that the average bit life was about 25 meters. Improvements would certainly better the performance but present performance cannot be considered poor.

A comparison of US and USSR average drilling speeds for 1955 illustrates that although the Soviet bit when on bottom was making 2.6 times as much hole, the performance of the US bit, in terms of meters per rig-month, was far superior. This latter advantage rests with the US because the Soviet bit cannot stand up under the high rates of penetration imparted by the turbodrill. Thus the time consumed in the frequent bit changes negates to a certain extent the advantages of higher penetration rates. A time distribution of USSR drilling operations, covering 1956 and first-half 1957, is given in Table 15.

Drilling speeds obtained in development drilling have been more than double exploratory drilling speeds, but such speeds fell off by about 10 percent during 1958-59, probably because of poor bit performance. Sharp increases in both exploratory and development drilling speeds are planned for 1959-65, as illustrated in the following:

USSR Drilling Speeds
(Meters per Rig-Month)

Year	Exploratory	Development	Year	Exploratory	Development
1940	232.8	413.6	1957	401.0	1,082.0
1945	184.9	319.2	1958	417	1,084
1950	208.7	629.4	1959	419	996
1955	305.7	893.3	1965		
1956	336.8	942.9	Plan	780	1,767

Table 15

USSR Time Distribution of Drilling Operations
1956 and First-Half 1957 Data

	Minutes	Percent of Total
Total Calendar Time per Meter Drilled	80.4	100.0
Productive Time		
Bit on bottom	8.4	10.4
Running in and out	12.6	15.7
Casing	4.2	5.2
Secondary Operations	21.0	26.1
Total	46.2	57.5
Non-Productive Time		
Repairs	5.4	6.7
Liquidation of complications	5.4	6.7
Accidents	7.8	9.7
Downtime	15.6	19.4
Total	34.2	42.5

The number of drilling rigs in operation in the USSR has been declining in recent years. This decline has been brought about by increases in the annual productivity of the drilling rigs, which have more than equalled the growth in annual volumes of exploratory and development drilling.

Year	Meters/rig/year	Number of Rigs in Use
1940	4,880	399
1945	2,027	262
1950	3,966	1,079
1955	5,800	871
1956	6,207	820
1957	7,243	850
1958	7,303	943

The necessity for maintaining and even increasing the production of crude oil in such older areas as Baku and Sakhalin Island has forced the USSR to enter into the phase of deep-drilling probably earlier than anticipated.

The deepest producing well in the USSR was completed in the summer of 1960, at a depth of 4,895 meters. This well, located in Baku, was drilled with a turbodrill and completed with diamond bits. The deepest offshore well, an exploratory effort in the Caspian Sea one kilometer off the Karadag coast, was drilled to a depth of 4,414 meters. Plans for 1960 called for the sinking of a 7,000 meter well at the Karadag gas-condensate deposit in Azerbayd-zhan, using combined rotary-turbodrilling. A total of 120 wells with depths ranging between 5,000 to 5,300 meters are to be drilled in Azerbaydzhan during 1959-65. Long-range plans for expansion of production in Azerbayd-zhan call for 6,000 to 10,000 meter wells to tap deep-lying strata.

Average well depths for the USSR on the whole have been increasing, largely reflecting deeper drilling in the Urals-Volga.

USSR Average Well Depths (Meters)

Year	Exploratory	Development
1940	1,108	940
1946	1,201	1,021
1950	1,349	1,146
1955	1,748	1,454
1956	1,790	1,449
1957	1,834	1,478
1958	1,857	1,607

B. Costs

Considerable regional variation exists within the USSR in the costs of exploratory and development drilling. For example, the cost for each meter of exploratory drilling in 1958 averaged 1,083 rubles, but by region varied from a low of 716 rubles in the Tatar ASSR to 2,197 rubles per meter on Sakhalin Island (see Table 16). A similar situation prevailed for development drilling costs which averaged 465 rubles per meter in 1958, but which by region fluctuated from 392 rubles per meter in Azerbaydzhan to 781 rubles per meter in Kirgiz.

Table 16

Regional Costs of Drilling in the USSR
1958
(1 July 1955 Rubles per Meter)

Region	Exploratory Drilling	Development Drilling
RSFSR	1,060	460
Bashkir ASSR	740	536
Tatar ASSR	716	415
Kuybyshev Oblast	1,222	534
Sakhalin Island	2,197	688
Azerbaydzhan SSR	1,213	392
Turkmen SSR	1,436	620
Ukraine SSR	1,020	748
Uzbek SSR	843	555
Kirgiz SSR	1,158	781

USSR costs for all wells drilled in 1958 averaged 760 rubles per meter or 231.6 rubles per foot. For comparison, the costs of drilling of all wells in the US in 1959 were reported at $US 12.90 per foot. This comparison yields a ruble-dollar ratio of 18-1. A much lower ruble-dollar ratio is apparent for offshore drilling costs. US offshore drilling costs averaged $US 38.34 per foot in 1959; USSR offshore drilling costs (Baku) approached 1,100 rubles per meter, the equivalent of 335.3 rubles per foot, in 1958, for a ruble-dollar ratio of about 8.7-1.

Some difficulty has been encountered in the USSR in an attempt to reduce the average costs of drilling. As shown in Table 17, both exploratory and development costs were higher in 1958 than in 1957. A considerable decline

Table 17

Costs of Drilling in the USSR
1950, 1955-58 and 1965 Plan
(1 July 1955 Rubles per Meter)

Year	Exploratory Drilling	Development Drilling
1950	1,182	456
1955	1,366	484
1957	1,069	456
1958	1,083	465
1965 Plan	820	359

in costs of drilling is anticipated by 1965 through higher drilling speeds and increases in rig and worker productivity.

C. Volumes

Steady increases have been maintained in the annual volumes of exploratory and development drilling in the USSR. These volumes are far below those needed in the US to find and develop producing capacity. To illustrate, during the period 1946-59 the USSR drilled approximately 64.2 million meters of exploratory and development holes, which represented only one-twelfth of the volume drilled in the US in the same time period. However, for the USSR the result was an increase in production from 19.4 million tons to 129.5 million tons plus an increase in the extraction of natural gas from 3.3 billion cubic meters to 35.4 billion cubic meters per year. The performance of the Soviet petroleum industry during the years 1946-59 exceeded the US performance during the period 1918-1930.

In 1959, for the first time the annual volume of exploratory drilling exceeded that of development drilling. This shift was preserved in 1960, but the plan for exploratory drilling in that year was sharply underfulfilled. An increase of more than 25 percent in exploratory drilling is planned for 1961, but only 5 percent for development drilling. The continued emphasis on exploratory drilling reflects the desire to expand the base to provide for continued increases in the production of crude oil and natural gas through additions to proved reserves. Although the plans for increments to proved reserves of crude oil have been met for the most part, significant and sometimes above-plan growths have been achieved with respect to additions to proved reserves of natural gas. These growths are shown in the following tabulation (in billion cubic meters):

Year	Non-Associated Natural Gas Reserves	Increment Actual	Plan
1955	490.1	107.1	75
1956	588	98.4	84
1957	700	134.0	116
1958	988	316.9	202
1959	1,684	713	359
1960	1,911	272	396

Annual volumes of exploratory and development drilling for oil and gas in the USSR during 1940, 1946-60 and that planned for 1961 and 1965 are shown in Table 18.

Table 18

Drilling for Oil and Gas in the USSR
1940, 1946-60 and 1961 and 1965 Plans
(Thousand Meters)

Year	Exploratory	Development	Total
1940	531.0	1,416	1,947.0
1946	577.7	651.2	1,228.9
1947	847.2	1,065.4	1,912.6
1948	1,219.8	1,572.9	2,792.7
1949	1,598.6	2,076.6	3,775.2
1950	2,127.3	2,155.3	4,282.6
1951	2,375.2	2,332.0	4,707.2
1952	2,279.2	2,625.8	4,905.0
1953	2,481.6	2,880.3	5,361.9
1954	2,267.6	2,672.7	4,940.2
1955	2,241.8	2,770.5	5,012.3
1956	2,314.0	2,775.0	5,090.0
1957	2,868.3	3,288.2	6,156.5
1958	3,369	3,518	6,887
1959	3,762	3,386	7,148
1960 Plan	4,608	3,516	8,124
1960 Actual	4,050	3,700	7,750
1961 Plan	5,100	3,900	9,000
1965 Plan	10,112	5,930	16,042

The larger share of exploratory drilling in the USSR is directed toward the finding and developing of new crude oil capacity, but as illustrated in Table 19, the trend since 1955 indicates a growing priority given to exploratory drilling for natural gas.

In contrast, very minor volumes of development drilling have been directed to the natural gas industry, largely because of the extremely high productivity of natural gas wells. For example, Soviet sources indicate that the approximately 7 billion cubic meters of natural gas produced at the Shebelinka deposit in the eastern Ukraine was provided by only 40 wells. The distribution of development drilling between oil and gas for selected years 1940-60 is shown in Table 20.

Soviet experts claim that the success of their petroleum industry in the finding of new deposits of crude oil is due largely to the policy of concentrating exploratory drilling in the most favorable areas and curtailing the number of areas under exploration. Since 1951, the number of areas under exploration has declined sharply, while the volume of drilling in each area has continued to increase. For example, in the Caucasus in 1951, a total of 201 areas were under exploration, with an average of 5,000 meters of exploratory drilling devoted to each area. By 1956 the number of areas under exploration in the Caucasus had been reduced to 81, but drilling per area had risen to 7,400 meters.

The exploration program in the Soviet Union generally is characterized by three stages. These stages are: 1) structures are explored that are relatively shallow but promising; 2) buried structures and deep horizons are explored; 3) drilling of the remaining structures. Some deviation from this approach is permitted, of course. It is claimed by Soviet authorities that

Table 19

Exploratory Drilling in the USSR for Crude Oil and Natural Gas
1940, 1946-60 and Plans for 1961 and 1965
(Thousand Meters)

Year	Crude Oil	Natural Gas	Total
1940	502	29	531
1946	552.6	25.1	577.7
1947	814.3	32.9	847.2
1948	1,141.8	78.0	1,219.8
1949	1,585.8	112.8	1,698.6
1950	1,980.3	147.0	2,127.3
1951	2,155.2	220	2,375.2
1952	2,172.2	107	2,279.2
1953	2,206.6	275	2,481.6
1954	1,994.5	273	2,267.5
1955	2,006.8	235	2,241.8
1956	1,999.0	315	2,314.0
1957	2,266.3	602	2,868.3
1958	2,623.0	746	3,369
1959	2,777.0	985.0	3,762
1960 Plan	3,313	1,295	4,608
1960 Actual	na	na	4,050
1961 Plan	na	na	5,100
1965 Plan	na	na	10,112

Table 20

Development Drilling for Crude Oil and Natural Gas in the USSR
1940 and 1946-60
(Thousand Meters)

Year	Crude Oil	Natural Gas	Total
1940	1,390.0	26.0	1,416.0
1946	644.8	6.4	651.2
1947	1,040.9	24.5	1,065.4
1948	1,548.3	24.6	1,572.9
1949	2,056.2	20.4	2,076.6
1950	2,124.0	31.3	2,155.3
1951	2,320.9	11.1	2,332.0
1952	2,588.6	37.2	2,625.8
1953	2,857.5	22.8	2,880.3
1954	2,647.4	25.3	2,672.7
1955	2,729.3	41.2	2,770.5
1956	2,272.0	48.0	2,775.0
1957	na	na	3,288.2
1958	na	na	3,518
1959	na	na	3,386
1960 Plan	na	na	3,516
1960 Actual	na	na	3,700

the exploratory program has been responsible for the discovery of about 400 oil fields and 186 gas fields.

Much of the sedimentary area of the USSR remains for detailed exploratory work. In particular, little drilling has been carried out in Siberia, Central Asia, or in the Caspian depression. The areas of highest density of exploratory drilling per area of sedimentary cover are found in the older producing areas of Azerbaydzhan and in parts of the North Caucasus region. In these regions the density (based on 1920-58 data) averages almost 232 meters of exploratory drilling per square kilometer of sedimentary cover in the Chechen-Ingush ASSR in the North Caucasus and about 133 meters per square kilometer in Azerbaydzhan. In contrast, the density averages only 0.18 meters per square kilometer for all of Siberia, which has a sedimentary cover of almost 5.5 million square kilometers. For the USSR as a whole, the density is only 3.08 meters per square kilometer of sedimentary cover. The density of exploratory drilling in the USSR by region, covering total exploratory drilling for per period 1920-58 is given in Table 21.

A major effort is to be exerted during 1959-65 to explore in greater detail the sedimentary areas of the USSR. The exploratory drilling program for these years calls for a total of 49,140,000 meters, of which 10,112,000 meters are planned for 1965 alone. An examination of these plans by region and republic indicates a serious attempt to explore crude oil possibilities in Central Asia and to a lesser extent, in Siberia, the Soviet Far East and in the Komi ASSR (the Soviet North). But again, the bulk of the exploratory drilling will be directed toward the opening of crude oil deposits in the Urals-Volga. The plan for exploratory drilling in the USSR during 1959-65, as apportioned among the various republics and by major oil-producing region within the RSFSR, is as follows:

Republic	Thousand Meters		Percent of Total	
RSFSR	31,030		63.1	
Urals		7,044		14.3
Volga		10,861		22.1
N. Caucasus and				
Astrakhan Oblast		8,068		16.4
Siberia, Far East				
and Komi ASSR		4,655		9.5
Other		402		0.8
Azerbaydzhan	2,900		5.9	
Ukraine	5,000		10.2	
Belorussia	150		0.3	
Uzbek	3,000		6.1	
Kirgiz	600		1.2	
Kazakh	2,000		4.1	
Turkmen	3,300		6.7	
Georgia	250		0.5	
Other	910		1.9	
Total	49,140		100.0	

Table 21

Density of Exploratory Drilling in the USSR
1920-58

Area	Exploratory Drilling (Thousand Meters)	Area of Sedimentary Cover (Thousand Sq. km)	Density of Drilling for Sedimentary Cover (meters/sq. km)	Avg. depth of Exploratory wells (meters)	
				1956	1957
USSR	33,866	11,000	3.08	1,800	1,834
RSFSR*	20,926	7,140	2.93	1,846	1,830
Urals-Volga	10,742	684.2	15.69	–	–
Tatar ASSR	1,914	67.6	28.31	1,799	1,767
Kuybyshev Obl.	1,830	53.8	34.01	1,609	1,840
Saratov Obl.	1,041	100.2	10.39	2,029	2,079
Stalingrad Obl.	865	114.1	7.58	1,738	1,645
Bashkir ASSR	3,314	84.3	39.90	1,727	1,705
Perm' Obl.	919	134.1	6.85	1,852	1,739
Orenburg Obl.	608	86.8	7.00	2,042	1,900
Penza Obl.	251	43.3	5.80	–	–
North Caucasus	7,743	249.9	29.78	–	–
Chechen-Ingush ASSR	3,015	13.0	231.92	2,572	1,983
Dagestan ASSR	767	23.2	33.06	1,940	1,975
Krasnodar Kray	2,967	62.5	47.47	2,229	2,165
Stavropol' Kray	694	151.2	4.59	1,414	2,122
Sakhalin Island	829	74.1	11.19	1,408	1,630
Siberia	922	5,460	0.18	–	–
Komi ASSR	779	363.2	2.14	1,183	1,238
Azerbaydzhan SSR	6,566	49.5	132.6	2,310	2,170
Ukraine SSR	1,719	400.0	4.30	1,869	1,900
Belorussia SSR	219	207.6	1.05	3,026	3,121
Uzbek SSR	1,228	359.4	3.42	1,720	1,586
Tadzhik SSR	–	25.0	–	–	–
Kirgiz SSR	209	18.2	11.48	2,027	1,943
Kazakh SSR	1,578	1,805.9	0.87	1,208	1,477
Turkmen SSR	1,088	450.0	2.42	2,204	2,071
Georgian SSR	525	29.9	17.56	2,566	1,421

*Some minor areas within the RSFSR have been omitted.

X. PRODUCTION OF CRUDE OIL

A. Historical Background

Up to the early 1870's all of the Russian crude was collected from hand-dug pits, averaging about 50 feet in depth. A. Beeby Thompson wrote that in in the year 1871 the first oil well in Russia was drilled, on the Balakhany plateau, although recently Soviet writers have been claiming a much earlier date, one preceding the Drake well.

The extraction of crude oil from these pits through the use of buckets averaged about 200,000 puds* during the years 1818-1857. At this point, extraction began to increase steadily and reached 132,000 tons in 1875. By 1901, Russia was the leading producer of crude oil in the world, the extraction of crude oil in that year having reached 11,562,000 tons, or 47 percent of total world production. Following this peak, a combination of a number of factors, but primarily reflecting the vast labor unrest in Baku which gave rise to destruction of facilities and the constant cessation of operations, served to depress the growth in production of crude oil in Russia. By 1905 the output of crude had fallen to 7,666,000 tons.

An industrial surge in czarist Russia, beginning in 1908, stimulated the production of crude oil for several years and, coupled with increased requirements resulting from Russian participation in World War I, a portion of the lost production was restored, as output reached approximately 10 million tons in 1916. But the uncertainty of the war effort and the communist revolution in 1917 cut short this growth. In 1917, the last year of czarist Russia, output of crude oil had declined to 8.8 million tons.

The overthrow of the czarist regime did not signal a return to domestic tranquility. Plagued by a disruptive civil war and hampered by radical changes in its administration, the petroleum industry fell further into economic despair, until by 1920 the extraction of crude oil had declined to 3.8 million tons.

The so-called New Economic Policy (N.E.P.), instituted by Lenin and covering the years 1921 through 1927, restored some of the personal freedom and initiative necessary for a revival in agricultural and industrial production. The close of this period found the output of crude restored to its previous annual high of 11.6 million tons.

The N.E.P. was displaced by the initiation of a state-planned economy, as the Soviet Union embarked on its First Five Year Plan, covering the years 1928-32, as shown in Figure 7. Gradually, but painfully at times, new pipelines were laid, new refineries built and old refineries rebuilt, new markets were created, both internally and externally, all of which supported an expansion in the production base. At the time of the invasion by the German military forces, the Soviet Union was in the midst of the Third Five Year Plan (1938-42), which had as one of its goals the production of 47.5 million tons of crude oil by 1942. The planned distribution of this production by

---

*One pud equals 36 pounds.

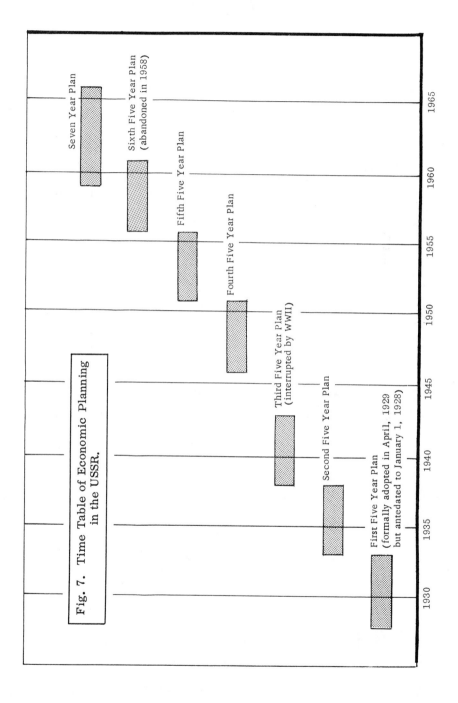

Fig. 7. Time Table of Economic Planning in the USSR.

region was to have been as follows (in millions of tons):

Area	1942 Planned Production
Caucasus	35.45
Eastern regions	10.34
Inc. Urals-Volga	7.0
Central Asia	1.71
Total	47.5

In the last year of at least a partially peaceful economy, 1941, the output of crude had increased to 33 million tons.

Because of the loss of the oil territories of Baku, Groznyy, and Maykop in the early stages of the war, attention was forced to the development of a production base in the eastern regions of the country. Early exploration efforts did not produce satisfactory results and differences in opinions among the various groups of geologists led to wasted time and effort. It was not until 1944 that the major discovery with respect to the creation of a new oil base in the eastern regions of the country was brought about. This came with the completion of well #100, at Tuymazy, which produced from the Devonian at a depth of 1,750 meters and with a daily yield of 250 metric

Photo No. 9. Well No. 100, Discovered in 1944, the First to
Produce from the Devonian in the Urals-Volga.

tons. By 1945, Devonian crude accounted for 24 percent of the total production from the Urals-Volga.

B. Regional Distribution

1. The Shift to the Urals-Volga

The immensity of the Urals-Volga oil-bearing region and the success
achieved in the exploitation of these deposits did not come as a total sur-
prise. At the 18th Congress of the Communist Party in 1939, V.M. Molotov
called for the creation of a new petroleum base — a second Baku — in the
region between the Volga River and the Ural Mountains. The area of this
new oil base was estimated to cover 1 million square kilometers, compared
with 10 thousand square kilometers for the "First Baku". Implementation
of this directive was to have raised the share of the eastern regions of the
country in the total production of crude oil to 21.8 percent. Some internal
opposition was voiced against the proposal of establishing the Second Baku,
for not all geologists were in agreement concerning its potential. Chief
among the proponents of the Second Baku was geologist I.M. Gubkin. His
theories on the presence of crude oil in the vast area between the Volga
River and the Ural Mountains were borne out in April, 1929, with the first
commercial production from the western slope of the Urals.

Despite the concentration of men and material in the Urals-Volga during
1942–45 in an effort to speed up discoveries of crude oil, production of crude
from this area in these years was considerably less than than anticipated,
as shown in the following:

Year	Production of Crude Oil From the Urals-Volga (Thousand metric tons)	Urals-Volga Production as a Percent of the National Total
1938	1,290	4.3
1939	1,934	6.4
1940	1,837	5.9
1942 Plan	7,000	14.7
1945	2,833	19.4
1946	3,900	21.4

It was not until after the close of the war that full advantage of the potential of the Urals-Volga was taken. Probably the most significant discovery
in the Urals-Volga during the ten-year period 1946-55 was the opening of
the Romashkino deposit, in the Tatar ASSR. This particular oil field has
been described by Soviet authorities as being, in terms of reserves, not
only the largest in the USSR, but in the world. Supported by this discovery
and by others of lesser extent, the yield of crude oil from the Urals-Volga
began to increase at an extremely rapid pace. As a portion of total national
output, that from the Urals-Volga increased to 29 percent in 1950 and to
58.7 percent by 1955. Further increases were registered during 1956-60,
to about 70 percent of the USSR total. It is estimated that by 1965, almost
80 percent of the Soviet production of crude oil in that year will come from
fields in the Urals-Volga. Producing fields of the Urals-Volga, according to
those administrative areas which together constitute the Urals-Volga area,
are shown in map no. 4. Production of crude oil in the USSR for the years
1860-1960 and that planned for 1961 is shown in Table 22.

Although the production of crude oil in the USSR has increased by more

Map No. 4. Urals-Volga Oil Fields
A — Oil and Gas Deposits of the Tatar ASSR

1 — Vishnevopolyanskoye
2 — Aksubayevskoye
3 — Nurlatskoye
4 — Novo-Sheshminskoye
5 — Novo-ibraykinskoye
6 — Ul'yanovskoye
7 — Staro-Bagryazhkoye
8 — Cheremshanskoye
9 — Ashal'chinskoye
10 — Shegurchinskoye

11 — Aksaranskoye
12 — Luzinskoye
13 — Krasnoyarskoye
14 — Popovskoye
15 — Aktashskoye
16 — Novo-Elkhovskoye
17 — Romashkinskoye
18 — Aznakayevskoye
19 — Muslyumovskoye

20 — Urzamet'evskoye
21 — Altupinskoye
22 — Oykinskoye
23 — Shugurovskoye
24 — Krym-Sarayskoye
25 — Bavlinskoye
26 — Sullinskoye
27 — Grakhovskoye
28 — Elabuzhskoye
29 — Bondyuzhskoye

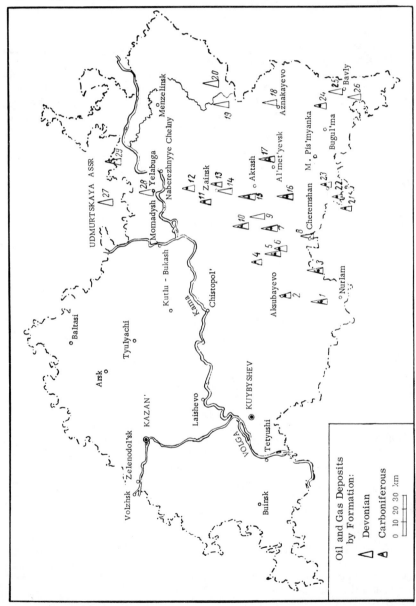

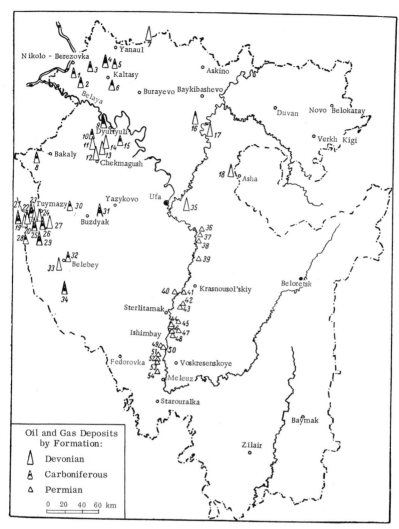

Map No. 4. Urals-Volga Oil Fields
B — Oil and Gas Deposits of the Bashkir ASSR

1 — Arlanskoye
2 — Urtaul-skoye
3 — Akineevskoye
4 — Or'ebashevskoye
5 — Cheraul'skoye
6 — Nadezhdinskoye
7 — Yugomashevskoye
8 — Bakalinskoye
9 — Dyurtyulinskoye
    (Ivanaevskoye)
10 — Mancharovskoye
11 — Tam'yanovskoye
12 — Chekmagushevskoye
13 — Sarybashevskoye
14 — Novoural'skoye
15 — Santovskoye
16 — Kushkul'skoye
17 — Krasno-Klyu-
    chevskoye
18 — Kul'tyubinskoye
19 — Aleksandrovskoye

20 — Yuzhno-Mullinskoye
21 — Oktyabr'skoye
22 — Tuymazinskoye
23 — Verkhne-Zaitovskoye
24 — Leonidovskoye and
    Yuzhno-Leonidovskoye
26 — Serafinovskoye
27 — Konstantinovskoye
28 — Staroturaevskoye
29 — Stakhanovskoye and
    Yakshevskoye
30 — Kopey-Kubovskoye
31 — Kargalinskoye
32 — Belebeevskoye
33 — Aksakovskoye
34 — Shkapovskoye
35 — Turbaslinskoye
36 — Irnykshin
37 — Malyshevskoye
38 — Kartashov

39 — Sarikovskoye
40 — Kuganakskoye
41 — Karlinskoye
42 — Burunovskoye
43 — Tsvetayevskoye
44 — Kusyapkulovskoye
45 — Salikhovskoye
46 — Ishimbayskaya gruppa
    mestorozhdeniy-
    massivy Zapadnyy,
    Vostochnyy, Yuzh-
    nyy, Buranchinskiy
    Kuz'minovskiy;
47 — Kinzebulatovskoye
48 — Ter'men'-Eglinskoye
49 — Stolyarovskoye
50 — Severo-Zirganskoye
51 — Vvedenovskoye
52 — Yuzhno-Vvedenovskoye
53 — Terekshinskoye
54 — Kazankovskoye

Map No. 4. Urals-Volga Oil Fields
C — Oil and Gas Deposits of the Kuybyshev Oblast'

1 — Zaborovskoye	15 — Studenoklyu-	28 — Chernovskoye
2 — Syzranskoye	chevskoye	29 — Vostochno-Chernovskoye
3 — Gubinskoye	16 — Chesnokovskoye	30 — Mikhaylovskoye
4 — Karlovo-	17 — Borovskoye	31 — Kozhemyakskoye
Sytovskoye	18 — Sernovodskoye	32 — Novo-Klyuchevskoye
5 — Berezovskoye	19 — Yakushkinskoye	33 — Kokhanskoye
6 — Yablonovyy ovrag	20 — Shungutskoye	34 — Yablonevskoye
7 — Zhigulevskoye	21 — Buz-Bash	35 — Kuvayskoye
8 — Strel'nyy ovrag	22 — Anlinskoye	36 — Gorodetsko
9 — Zol'nyy ovrag	23 — Deryuzhevskoye	37 — Novo-Gorodetskoye
10 — Pokrovskoye	24 — Amanakskoye	38 — Skobelevskoye
11 — Krasnoyarskoye	25 — Kalinovskoye	39 — Zhukovskoye
12 — Sergiyevskoye	26 — Mukhanovskoye	40 — Neklyudovskoye
13 — Malinovskoye	27 — Dmitrievskoye	41 — Novo-Zhukovskoye
14 — Radayevskoye	and Luganskoye	42 — Sosnovskoye

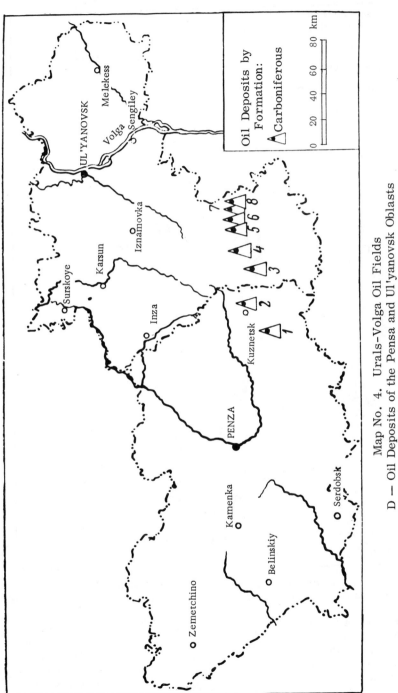

Map No. 4. Urals-Volga Oil Fields
D — Oil Deposits of the Pensa and Ul'yanovsk Oblasts

1 — Verkhozimskoye   3 — Baranovskoye   5 — Golodyaevskoye   7 — Novo-Tamyshevskoye
2 — Komarovskoye   4 — Varvarovskoye   6 — Novo-Spasskoye   8 — Rep'evskoye

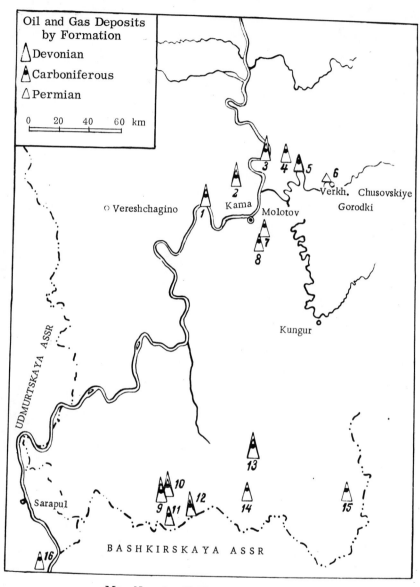

Map No. 4. Urals-Volga Oil Fields
E — Oil and Gas Deposits of the Molotov Oblast' and the Udmurt ASSR

1 — Krasnokamskoye	6 — Chusovskiye Gorodki	12 — Kuedinskoye
2 — Severokamskoye	7 — Lobanovskoye	13 — Tanykskoye
3 — Polazninskoye	8 — Kozubayevskoye	14 — Pavlovskoye
4 — Yarinskoye	9 — Gozhanskoye	15 — Kamenskoye
5 — Shalashinskoye	10 — Brykinskoye	16 — Vyatskoye
	11 — Gondryevskoye	

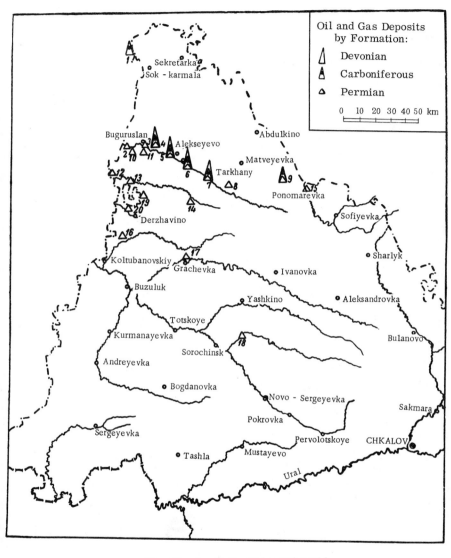

Map No. 4. Urals-Volga Oil Fields
F — Oil and Gas Deposits of the Chkalov Oblast'

1 — Baytuganskoye
2 — Zhuralevsko-
    Stepanovskoye
3 — Buguruslanskoye
4 — Krasnoyarskoye
5 — Zaglyadinskoye
6 — Sultangulovskoye
7 — Tarkhanskoye
8 — Ashironskoye
9 — Yefremovo-
    Zykovskoye
10 — Kiryushinskoye
11 — Bashkatovskoye
12 — Sadkinskoye
13 — Pilyuginskoye
14 — Osinovskoye
15 — Ponomarevskoye
16 — Mogutovskoye
17 — Grachevskoye
18 — Sorochinskoye
19 — Ivanovskoye
20 — Marasinskoye

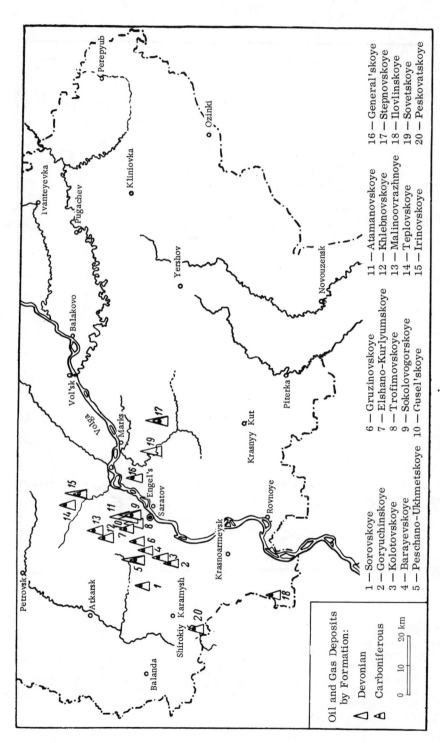

Map No. 4.   Urals–Volga Oil Fields;   G — Oil and Gas Deposits of the Saratov Oblast'

Map No. 4. Urals-Volga Oil Fields
H — Oil and Gas Deposits of the Stalingrad Oblast'

1 — Verkhovskoye   6 — Abramovskoye
2 — Saushinskoye   7 — Korobkovskoye
3 — Panikskoye   8 — Zhirnovskoye
4 — Archedinskoye   9 — Linevskoye
5 — Vetyutnevskoye   10 — Bakhmet'evskoye

Table 22

Production of Crude Oil in the USSR
1860-1960 and 1961 Plan

Year	Thousand Metric Tons	Year	Thousand Metric Tons	Year	Thousand Metric Tons	Year	Thousand Metric Tons
1860	4	1886	1,896	1912	9,292	1938	30,186
1861	4	1887	2,360	1913	9,234	1939	30,259
1862	4	1888	3,013	1914	9,176	1940	31,121
1863	6	1889	3,281	1915	9,442	1941	33,000
1864	9	1890	3,778	1916	9,970	1942	22,000
1865	9	1891	4,527	1917	8,800	1943	18,000
1866	13	1892	4,690	1918	4,146	1944	18,300
1867	17	1893	5,530	1919	4,448	1945	19,436
1868	29	1894	4,916	1920	3,851	1946	21,746
1869	42	1895	6,745	1921	3,781	1947	26,022
1870	33	1896	6,795	1922	4,658	1948	29,249
1871	26	1897	7,275	1923	5,277	1949	33,444
1872	27	1898	8,331	1924	6,064	1950	37,878
1873	68	1899	8,958	1925	7,061	1951	42,253
1874	86	1900	10,378	1926	8,318	1952	47,311
1875	132	1901	11,562	1927	10,285	1953	52,777
1876	191	1902	11,080	1928	11,625	1954	59,281
1877	253	1903	10,415	1929	13,684	1955	70,793
1878	334	1904	10,888	1930	18,451	1956	83,806
1879	403	1905	7,556	1931	22,392	1957	98,346
1880	352	1906	8,171	1932	21,414	1958	113,216
1881	663	1907	8,655	1933	21,489	1959	129,557
1882	827	1908	8,739	1934	24,218	1960	147,864
1883	991	1909	9,296	1935	25,218	1961	164,000
1884	1,479	1910	9,626	1936	27,427	Plan	
1885	1,905	1911	9,176	1937	28,501		

than 7.6 times since the end of the war, the number of active oil wells has increased by less than 3 times. Furthermore, it is probable that the total number of oil wells in the USSR, both active and inactive, has only slightly more than doubled in the fourteen-year period since 1946.

As shown in Table 23, there were 33,900 active wells in the USSR in 1960, compared with 11,600 active wells in 1946. Not all of the growth in the number of active wells during these years represented new effort. A sizeable group of the now-active wells represents the successful restoration to production of wells which previously had been shut down for various reasons. In the prewar years, because of a lack of either labor or material, it was not possible in a number of fields to bring back into production those wells which had been shut down because of mechanical breakdowns, excessive water flooding or other reasons. These wells were then listed as inactive. Under the classification system currently in use, a well is considered to be active, no matter what the reason for cessation of production. Only if it is considered economically inexpedient to continue the exploitation of the well, is this well taken off the active list.

Number of Oil Wells in the USSR, Selected Years 1946-60.   Table 23

Year	Prod. of Crude Oil (Million Metric Tons)	Production Per Active Well (Metric Tons)	Number of Active Wells*	Active Wells as Percent of All Wells	Total Wells*
1946	21.7	1,872	11,600	65.0	17,800
1950	37.7	2,016	18,800	na	na
1951	42.3	1,968	21,500	na	na
1955	70.8	2,568	27,600	89.5	30,800
1958	113.2	3,708	30,500	87.8	34,700
1959	129.6	4,050	32,000	na	na
1960	147.9	4,368	33,900	na	na

*Rounded [to the nearest hundred].

At the beginning of 1959 the USSR held 2,000 wells on the inactive list, placed there in past years under the old classification scheme, which were still capable of producing crude.* Approximate calculations made by Soviet planners indicated that the return of these inactive wells to exploitation would allow an increase in total annual production of crude oil of about 2 million tons per year. Soviet figures showed that the productivity of each of these inactive wells was calculated at about 20 barrels per day or 1,000 tons per year..

Attention also is being given to raising the coefficient of utilization of active wells. During the period 1940-55 the coefficient of utilization increased sharply — from 0.907 to 0.955, as a result of lengthening of the time interval between repairs and a reduction in the length of time shut down for repairs. During 1956-58 the coefficient of utilization was stabilized at the level of 0.955 to 0.958.

Thus, if the USSR considers it economically expedient to restore to production at least a portion of those wells which once had been considered inactive and if the coefficient of utilization of the active wells can be raised somewhat, then, to these extents the USSR does have some shut-in production.

Average well productivity in the USSR continues to show rather rapid growth, having increased from 2,568 tons per year in 1955 (about 51 barrels per day) to 4,368 tons per year in 1960 (87 barrels per day). On the other hand, a significant number of active oil wells in the USSR produce less than 1 barrel per day. In 1954, the most recent year for which data are available, there were about 2,000 wells under exploitation in the USSR which yielded less than one-half barrel per day per well. The total annual output of crude oil from these wells was about 50,000 tons and the cost of production reached to 100 rubles and higher per ton.

The greatest concentration of low-productivity wells is found in Azerbaydzhan. In 1959 in Azerbaydzhan, a total of 2,565 low-yield wells were in production, each of which averaged about 1.6 barrels per day. Of the total of 2,565 wells, which represented almost 8.5 percent of all active wells in the Soviet Union, 1,081 wells averaged less than 0.8 barrels per day.

*Of these, about 64 percent are located in Azerbaydzhan.

2. Azerbaydzhan

Some growth has been recorded in the production of crude oil in recent years at Baku, but this growth has lagged far behind that of the Urals-Volga. Consequently, although production has increased from 11.5 million tons in 1945 to 17.8 million tons in 1960, the share of Baku production relative to the national total has declined steadily. The output of crude from the Tatar ASSR, the Bashkir ASSR and Kuybyshev Oblast, all in the Urals-Volga, each exceeds that from Azerbaydzhan. Although fulfillment of the Seven Year

Photo No. 10. Four Wells Drilled From One Set Up and Two Pumps With Twin Cables Pumping From Four Wells Simultaneously, Near Baku.

Plan goal would very nearly restore Baku production to its prewar high of 23.5 million tons, less meaning will be attached to this contribution, for by 1965 the output of crude from Azerbaydzhan will represent only about 8 percent of the national total.

3. Other

In addition to the Urals-Volga and Baku, crude oil is extracted in commercial quantities in the Ukraine, in Kazakhstan, and in the Central Asian republics of Turkmen, Uzbek, Tadzhik, and Kirgiz. Production also is reported for the Soviet Far North and on Sakhalin Island. At present, oil industry activity in East and West Siberia is limited to a major exploratory program, which so far has shown some degree of success. The first commercial showing of crude oil in Siberia was obtained in 1960, along the Ob' River in Tyumen' Oblast.

As shown in Table 24, production from Kazakhstan and the Central Asian republics, and from the Ukraine in relation to the national output, have been declining. Production data on the Soviet Far North and on Sakhalin Island are not reported separately, but are included in the total given for the RSFSR. The most recent Soviet reference to the output of crude oil in these

Table 24

Production of Crude Oil in the USSR by Republic
1950, 1955, 1958-60 and 1965 Estimate
(Thousand Metric Tons)

Republic	1950	1955	1958	1959	1960	1965 Estimate
RSFSR	18,231	49,263	87,978	102,792	118,900	220,360
Inc. Urals-Volga	10,985	41,555	76,000	90,000	104,000	210,000
Ukraine	293	531	1,236	1,627	2,159	6,000
Uzbek	1,342	996	1,297	1,465	1,601	3,000
Kazakh	1,059	1,397	1,511	1,544	1,601	2,000
Georgia	43	43	35	35	35	80
Azerbaydzhan	14,822	15,305	16,497	17,076	17,800	22,000
Kirgiz	47	115	490	424	464	464
Tadzhik	20	17	18	17	17	60
Turkmen	2,021	3,126	4,154	4,577	5,278	10,000
Total	37,878	70,793	113,216	129,557	147,864	265,000

areas stated that in 1956, the production of crude oil in the Far North was 587,000 tons and on Sakhalin Island — 1,006,000 tons. Based on percentage increases reported since that time, it may be reliably estimated that production of crude oil in the Far North by 1960 had increased to approximately 1 million tons, and on Sakhalin Island — to 1.5 million tons.

C. Notes on Oil Fields Visited by Delegation

1. Tuymazy-Oktyabrsk

The delegation reached Tuymazy by overnight train from Ufa. Hosts were:

Zhdanov, A.M.	— Chief, Oil Extraction Industry of Bashkir ASSR
Mironov, V.Ya.	— Chief
Pelevin, L.A.	— Assistant Chief Engineer
Nikitin, A.I.	— Chief Geologist
Knyazev, N.S.	— Chief, Oil Field No. 5
Gisak, P.A.	— Chief, Oil Field No. 6
Il'in, N.G.	— Chief Engineer, Tuymaza Oil Drilling Trust (Tuymazaburneft')
Golovtsov, M.V.	— Chief Engineer, Bashkir Oil and Gas Trust (Bashneftegaz)
Il'chenko, I.K.	— Chief of House of Technics of Tuymazaneft'

Location

On the River Ikh southwest of Ufa, in western Bashkir ASSR and eastern Tatar ASSR. Tuymazy is the old town on the railroad at the northeastern edge of the field.

Discovery Date

Carboniferous 1934; Devonian 1944.

Discovery Method

Surface structure mapped in upper Permian beds supported by a core drill program. It was stated that there a number of similar structures in the region, some producing, some tested but so far dry, some untested. Surface geology extended by stratigraphic drilling is the primary exploration method. Geophysics is not much used, but when it is, the seismograph is preferred. The near surface limestones are a seismic problem. When an anomaly is found it is systematically mapped by core holes.

Structure

An unfaulted, gently folded asymmetrical anticline, trending northeast-southwest. The steep flank is to the southeast. It covers 15 x 30 kilometers with a total closure of 80 meters at Devonian depths.

Stratigraphy

The generalized stratigraphic section shows carbonates dominant (98%) from 300 meters to crystaline basement of 1,865 meters. Limestone makes up the bulk but the section includes stringers of chert, fairly thick dolomites and the quartzitic producing sands. The type log shown indicated:

Early Carboniferous production	— 1,207 meters
Carboniferous-Devonian unconformity	— 1,298 meters
Devonian limestone production (not important)	— 1,360 meters
Zone I, main producer, sandstone, limestone and shale	— 1,720 to 1,745 meters
Zone II Devonian sandstone	— 1,775 meters
Basement, crystaline rocks	— 1,865 meters

Sands in Zone I blanket the area and vary in thickness from 2 to 20 meters; Zone II blanket sands vary from 5 to 30 meters. The average producible sands in Zones I and II combined is 40 meters. On the log shown basement was overlain by Devonian clay, but this is said to change to a sand facies in parts of the area, which has production possibilities.

Reservoir Characteristics

Porosity varies from 15 to 20 percent, permeability from 150 to 500 millidarcies with a few tight zones. Self potential and resistivity logs are used to spot porous intervals.

Spacing

Spacing for the presently unimportant Carboniferous production was not discussed. Zone I, now drilled up, has a 20 hectare spacing (400 x 500 meters); Zone II, 25 percent drilled up, is being developed at the same spacing. Some notes estimate 1,000 Devonian wells. At the spacing indicated this means that about half the 15 x 30 kilometer structure is productive which fits a claimed 40 meter oil column.

Production

34,000 metric tons per day, said to provide one-third of the total production of crude oil in Bashkiria. Almost all of the crude is Devonian. The 1944 discovery well is still producing 120 tons per day and has not yet had a workover.

Character of Crude

Specific gravity averages 0.855, sulphur content ranges from 2 percent as an average to as high as 3.5.

Pressure Maintenance

Drilling began on the gentle northeast flank, moving in toward the crest. Original reservoir pressure in 1944 was 172 atmospheres which fell to 110 by 1947 when water flooding began. Pressure is now back to 135 atmospheres and many wells formerly pumped are again flowing. The goal is to inject 1.7 units of water for each unit withdrawal. Specific gravity of the formation water is 1.19; fresh water from river sands is used for injection.

There are three water collection stations connected by a closed ring system draining water by gravity from wells within the flood plain of the River Ikh. Since the system is closed the water is not treated. Water is pumped from the collection sites to eleven pump stations from which injection wells are fed by constant pressure pump, total daily input being approximately 60,000 cubic meters. Input pressure is 80 kilograms per square centimeter; pump efficiencies are said to be 0.4 to 0.45. Water is injected on the periphery; the line of injection being 1.5 kilometers back from the nearest bank of producers. The flood advances at 50 meters a year. This implies, on the basis of spacing, a double bank of inactive wells between injection wells and producers. It was not determined why it was felt necessary to follow the production inward with the injection ring, or, similarly, why so many flank wells were drilled when a more or less static zone of injection wells complemented by a zone of the up-the-flank producers would seem to be enough. One member of the delegation offered the opinion that, because of the high rate of production, the benefits of flooding were not received at the crest of the structure, and that sizeable pockets of oil were being bypassed on the flanks.

Desalters

At least part of the crude is desalted and dehydrated in the field. The delegation was shown a plant having a 10,000 metric ton capacity per day, located about two kilometers east of the town of Oktyabrsk. Treatment is first chemical for emulsion breaking, then electrical, using the vertical-tank design seen in the Soviet refineries. Incoming fluid contains 20 percent salt water with a chlorinity of 60,000 milligrams per liter. Treatment reduces the water content to 0.2 percent and the salinity to 20 milligrams per liter.

Field Equipment

The field has been drilled almost entirely with the turbodrill although the electric bottom hole drill has also been used. Three turbo rigs are in operation now. The one inspected had a seven man crew; four is said to be the

Photo No. 11. Crude Oil Desalting Installation (Tuymazy-Oktyabrsk Oil Fields).

Photo No. 12. Exploratory Turbodrill Well in the Tuymazy-
Oktyabrsk Oil Fields. Note Wooden Ladder.

normal number. It was drilling at 750 meters and planned to go to 1,750.
Samples are customarily caught only through the pay section. The rig was
powered by electricity supplied by a central power station. Apparently the
Tuymazy-Oktyabrsk administration generates electric power for the entire
field and for the municipality. Practically all field functions, including
drilling and pumping, use it. Although the delegation had not been expected
at this rig, it was clean, equipment and supplies neatly arranged and the
crew demonstrated more esprit than was generally observed in Soviet
working groups.

At the depth given the crew reported 25 meters per bit in lime. Teeth on
the bits in the used stack were quite sharp, hence, it may be that the bear-
ings were worn. Eight minutes were required for a connection. Water was
being used as the drilling fluid, not mud. The rig was equipped with automatic breakout tongs and air activated slips. Similar equipment was seen
subsequently on the other three rigs visited during the tour. There were

Photo No. 13. Exploratory Turbodrill Well in the Tuymazy-Oktyabrsk Oil Fields. Showing Neatly Displayed Drilling Bits.

Photo No. 14. Compressor Station and Mud Pits for Pumping Drilling Fluid or Mud Through Turbodrill, at Tuymazy-Oktyabrsk Oil Fields.

Photo No. 15. Equipment for Electric Power Supply to Oil Field Area Showing
Contrast Between Power Equipment and Its Protection, at the
Tuymazy-Oktyabrsk Oil Fields.

Photo No. 16. Pumping Jack Similar to US Make, at the Tuymazy-Oktyabrsk
Oil Fields.

four men on a tour. The crew was using a separate set of elevators on the cat line for lifting the new joint and the kelly at the same time when making up a new connection as a time saving routine.

The water collection stations feed water to 11 injection stations each handling approximately 6,000 cubic meters per day through constant pressure pumps. Input pressure is 80 kilograms per square centimeter; pump efficiencies are 0.4 to 0.45.

Although water flooding has returned many wells to flowing, a large part of the area seen was on pump, typical counter-balanced beam types for the most part, but some were using Reda type submersibles. It was stated that all parts but one of the Reda type pump were made in the USSR. The equipment inspected was in good operating condition.

Pumping wells are operated on three phase, 380-volt power and are equipped with paraffin scrapers, rotating rods and automatic shut down devices.

Automation

Automatic slips and breakout tongs have been mentioned. In addition, the delegation was shown, on the Tatar side of the river, a radio central control station from which a dispatcher can monitor 170 wells. The initials L.U.R. were used in referring to the system. Eight or nine bands in the 39 to 46 megacycle range are used as carriers. Each band can be used to control twenty stations by modulation to the 300 to 4000 cycle audio band. The dispatcher can control power at each well, flow to storage (through stroke rate), storage balance, flow from storage, etc. Two way radio communication with almost one-third of these wells is available. The net will eventually include 300 wells.

The wells selected for radio control lie in the flood plain of the river Ikh which floods a north-south strip 1.5 to 3 kilometers in width across the field each spring. In flood time the wells can be serviced only by small boat.

Gas Pumping Station

The delegation visited one of nine units in a gas gathering system. It was equipped with conventional gas engine compressors and had a capacity of 250,000 cubic meters per day.

Gasoline Plant

The natural gasoline plant visited was conventional in design and was said to have an output of 850 to 1,000 tons of liquid and 2 million cubic meters of gas per day. It was built in stages, the first in 1951, the second in 1954, the last in 1958, at a reported total cost of 83 million rubles.

Miscellaneous

Local operating problems are:

a. Winter frost depth such that water flow lines are buried two meters.

b. Average snow cover late October to late April one meter, maximum three meters.

c. Summer to winter temperatures extremes 35°C to -47°C.

Insulation is a problem. A porous, diatomacious brick is used both outside and under cover. It does not stand up well but is said to be so cheap that it is the most economical thing to use.

2. Karadag (also referred to as Ninth Oil Field)

The delegation traveled by bus from Baku to Karadag where it met with the following:

Photo No. 17. Hydraulically Operated Break-Out Tool.

Photo No. 18. Hydraulically Operated Break-Out Tool.

Musayev, I.M.   — Chief Engineer of the Azerbaydzhan Oil Admin-
                     istration (Azneft'), and Member of the Azer-
                     baydzhan Economic Council
Babayev   — Production Engineer
Dimitriyev   — Geologist

Location
New Karadag lies on the western shore of the Caspian Sea, south of Baku
twenty-five or thirty kilometers, in the republic of Azerbaydzhan. The older

Photo No. 19. Slip Ring on Top of Drill Pipe Which Permits Drill Pipe
to be Rotated Yet Supplies Electricity to Electrodrill, at New Karadag.

producing Karadag area lies immediately inland.
Discovery Date
    1954 for New Karadag. The old production, also from the Pliocene, was
discovered in the thirties.
Discovery Method
    A combination of an unspecified electrical method and the seismograph.

Photo No. 20. Drill Pipe For Use by Electrodrill.

Structure
    Production is from a block on the south flank of a faulted anticline. The
major fault, a high angle thrust from the north and northeast, provides
closure in those directions. Fault throw is 300 meters at producing depths.
The structure map shown, which was probably somewhat schematic, indicated no structural closure to the west but there was a dry hole there. The
strike in the producing block is east-west; the section dips south expanding
rapidly in that direction.
Stratigraphy
    Mid-Pliocene sands and shales. The major producing section begins at
2,600 meters at the north part of the bloc where its thickness was said to
be 70 meters. It expands down dip to a thickness of 130 meters at a depth
of 4,500 meters. Here a thin oil ring above water is encountered. The main
producing zones are numbered VII and VIIa. Net effective sand thicknesses
in each zone were not given.
Reservoir Characteristics
    Porosity 17 percent; permeability 30 to 40 millidarcies.
Spacing
    One kilometer. The producing area covers 2,000 hectares but may ex-
pand.

Production

Figures in the notes of the delegates agree on 18 producing wells but figures for per well production range from 500,000 to 1,000,000 cubic meters gas per day and one hundred to one hundred and fifty tons of liquid. Some of these figures probably relate to actual production; others to what could be produced if desired. It is safe to say actual production is in excess

Photo No. 21. Rig Draw Works of an Electrodrill at the New Karadag Field.

of 600,000 cubic meters of gas, and 100 tons of condensate per well per day. A field total of 20,000 tons per day can be considered a minimum. Apparently production could be increased by 50 percent if required.

Characteristics of Oil

Specific gravity of the condensate is .77 to .778. One cubic meter of gas contains up to 170 grams of fluid. No sulfur is present.

Pressure Maintenance

None at present. In six years bottom hole pressure has dropped from 400 atmospheres to 360 atmospheres. Casing head pressure is about 280 atmospheres. The system can stand considerable further drop before repressuring is necessary.

Development

Moles of rock and earth have been built out into the Caspian Sea to reach offshore locations. Slant holes having maximum deviations of 20 degrees are drilled from these.

As part of the completion practice, pipe is set on bottom and perforated by a process described as burning. It may be a jet type perforation. As many as 100 holes per run can be made and three hundred holes per completion are sometimes required.

New Karadag has been drilled mainly by rotary but a turbodrill has been

Photo No. 22. Equipment on Turbodrill Well Just Off Derrick Floor at New Karadag.

Photo No. 23. Mud Handling Equipment (New Karadag).

brought in recently which is said to be making a cheaper hole than the rotary. Average penetration is 4 meters per hour for the first 3,000 meters, more or less twice the rotary rate.

In addition to the turbodrill a bottom-hole electric drill is being tried locally. The drill itself is 12 meters long and 20 centimeters in diameter.

Photo No. 24. High Pressure Gas Well at Karadag.

It operates on three phase power at 1,650 volts, draws 150 amperes and turns at 680 rpm. The swivel uses a commutator to supply the electric power to the drill through sections of electric cable mounted in each joint of drill pipe. The cable is co-axial, three conductor and each section is centrally held in its joint by plastic spiders. The female cable connector does not quite reach the end of the joint. The male connector extends past the tool joint threads but is protected by a steel sleeve. As the new joint is rotated to make up pipe in the hole the centered co-axial cable rotates and makes up in the connector. At New Karadag a 12 meter drill collar was being used and a weight of 14 tons was carried on the bit. The bit weight is automatically controlled. It was indicated that at shallow depths the electric drill was getting 700 meters per bit; at 2,100 meters, 30 meters per bit; at 3,000 meters 10 to 15 meters per bit. This is better than the stated performance for the turbodrill. Power was stepped down through a small transformer station from 6,000 transmission volts to the 1,650 volts needed.

While maximum inclination for deviated holes was said to be 20 degrees, it was also stated that experiments were in progress with 90 degree deviations — presumably for draining massive sands. Bottom hole temperatures were said to be 45° C at 2,000 meters, 90° C at 4,000 meters.

Gathering System

The gathering system operates into a series of separator stations, the first designed for a working pressure of 300 atmospheres. This stage extracts 98 percent of the liquids. Further stages continue the pressure drop to 20 atmospheres at the natural gasoline plant. The dry gas is presumably

used in the Baku area. Drip problems are eliminated by contour piping.
Personnel
The delegation was told there were 3,000 employees in the New and Old
Karadag administration to take care of 3,500 wells. Some 300 of the employees are classified as technical.
Miscellaneous
Apparently the local administration operates under an overall development plan worked out by the Azerbaydzhan sovnarkoz. Also subject to the
economic council are regional institutes or departments for production
(drilling), development (reservoir studies), geology, geophysics offshore
drilling (which handles offshore operations as a package), telemetering and
automation, refining and safety. Most of these departments have representative personnel in Karadag in functional advisory capacities, each
responsible to his central institute or department.
The older producing area was cluttered with standing steel derricks,
crown blocks, traveling blocks, used wire line, pipe, etc. in considerable
contrast with New Karadag.
In the old producing area a pair of pumps on the same slab were shown —
each horsehead operating two strings of rods. The two pumps were thus
pumping four slant holes.
The entire producing area, old and new, is electrified by a central power
system operated as part of the field administration for production purposes
and for use in the small city built for the personnel.
The delegation was informed that, in spite of the fact that Azerbaydzhan
was an old oil province, much exploration was being done and important
new discoveries were being made each year both in and around the Caspian
Sea.

3. Artyom

A brief visit was paid to the partially offshore Artyom Field. This trip
was offered in lieu of an offshore field which could be reached only by boat
or helicopter. The sea was too rough for boats on the scheduled day, but it
was not explained why the delegation was not offered the use of the helicop-
ters seen ferrying crews in and out to the offshore areas.
Location
At the northeast end of the Apsheron Peninsula about forty kilometers
east of Baku, in and on the shore of the Caspian Sea, in the Republic of
Azerbaydzhan.
Discovery Date
1947
Discovery Method
Probably an extension of onshore production.
Size
4 x 18 kilometers. On the basis of number of wells and spacing less than
half the structure is productive.
Structure
A sharply folded anticline trending northwest-southeast. Other similar
features are producing on the general trend far out to sea.
Stratigraphy
Miocene-Pliocene sands and shales.
Depth
1,800 to 2,000 meters.

Photo No. 25. Artyom Offshore (Caspian Sea).

Photo No. 26. Artyom Offshore (Caspian Sea).

Photo No. 27. Steel Sub-Structure of Offshore Trestles of Artyom Oil Field
in the Caspian Sea.

Photo No. 28. Gas Separation Station at Artyom Island.

Reservoir
    There are three main producing zones totaling 180 meters, one approxi-
mately 150 meters; the other two ranging from 10 to 20 meters each.
Probably not all of the thick sand can be considered net pay.

Spacing
    200 meters.

Production
    3,500 metric tons per day. Gas-oil ratio 50 to 60 cubic meters per ton.
Of the 750 wells in the field, 90 percent of the production comes from the
450 offshore wells. Hydrates are a production problem.

Pressure Maintenance
    Peripheral injection of Caspian Sea water. There are 90 injection wells.

Equipment
    Causeways and platforms are supported on steel piling. Average water
depth is 13 meters, maximum is 30. Piling is driven seven to ten meters
into bottom. Corrosion is noticeable but not as severe as might be expected
considering the high salinity of the Caspian. Concrete piling is to be used in
the near future. The part of the field connected by causeway to shore is
operated on centrally distributed electric power.
    Deviated holes are drilled (maximum 20 degrees) from causeway and
isolated offshore locations.

Personnel
    We were told there were 3,500 employees in the enterprise, 40 percent
women. Four hundred and sixty-five were rated as engineers or otherwise
technical. Very probably this large group handles offshore and onshore
producing areas other than Artyom.

Miscellaneous
    It was remarked that the level of the Caspian Sea had dropped two meters
within 25 years. This is apparently a long-term trend which is causing them
concern not only with respect to oil production but with respect to fisheries
and other industries.

4. Zhirnovsk

    Accompanied by several members of the Stalingrad Scientific and Re-
search Institute on Crude Oil and Natural Gas, the delegation traveled from
Stalingrad to the Zhirnovsk producing area, in two AN-2 ten-passenger bi-
planes. This was in lieu of a scheduled visit to the Archeda field,* which
was not considered feasible due to recent heavy rains. This field, we were
told, had not before been mentioned outside Soviet circles.

Location
    Three hundred kilometers north-northwest of Stalingrad on the Medved-
itsa River.

----

*Members of the Stalingrad Scientific and Research Institute stated that
Archeda lay about 100 kilometers west-northwest of Stalingrad; that the
structure consisted of a long, narrow, asymmetrical anticline having a steep
west flank; that the daily production was 1,000 tons from 11 Carboniferous
and Devonian horizons, the shallowest sands being at 500 meters. Eighty
percent of the production comes from Carboniferous and middle-to-upper
Devonian limestones. Lower Devonian was said to be absent. The field has
been drilled up for some time.

Discovery Date
1951
Discovery Method
The structure was originally found by surface work in 1896 in the middle Carboniferous beds exposed by the river. It was confirmed by a later detailed survey and by core drill. The feature is a Carboniferous inlier surrounded by Jurassic and Cretaceous.
Producing Structure
An asymmetrical, 2.5 x 6 kilometer anticline trending north-south. Dip on the east flank is from 1 to 2 degrees, on the west from 15 to 30 degrees. Other similar structures are in the region. One of these must lie north of Zhirnovsk, where several rigs were noted scattered over a 10-kilometer stretch. Also, three widely separated wildcats were seen on the flight south to Stalingrad, which fits the trend.
Stratigraphy
Carboniferous and Devonian limestones, with interbedded sands and shales.
Depth
1,100 meters to the main producing sands.
Reservoir
Eleven sands are said to be commercial in the Carboniferous and one or two in the Devonian. Only two are now being produced, both Carboniferous. The 1B sand, close to the base of the producible Carboniferous sands, accounts for 4,200 tons per day of the field total of 4,800 tons. The 1B sand is medium grained, averages fourteen meters in thickness, with a maximum of 25 meters. Sand thicknesses are variable without relation to position on the structure. The 1B sand is thin to absent at the south end of the structure. Permeability ranges from 300 to 5,000 millidarcies, the average being close to 1,000.

Apparently the Devonian has not been thoroughly explored. A test projected to 3,500 meters aimed at its evaluation was at 3,030 meters on the date of the visit. It had logged top of mid-Devonian at about 3,000 meters. This test is expected to find middle Devonian resting on basement.
Well Spacing
300 x 500 meters.
Production
There are 116 wells producing from the 1B sand. Production from this sand reached 5,000 tons per day by 1954; it was then cut back to 4,200 tons per day, the current figure. Production for the field is 4,800 tons per day. Wells are drilled by turbodrill, requiring two weeks for completion. Mechanical scrapers are used, operated automatically by wire line.
Character of Crude
Specific gravity of the crude is 0.86; it contains 0.2 percent sulphur; reservoir viscosity is 4 centiposes. Saturation pressure is 97 atmospheres; reservoir pressure, 102 atmospheres; the gas-oil ratio, 60 cubic meters per ton. The Devonian oil has a fairly high sulphur content.
Reserves
Eleven million tons have been produced from the 1B sand, which is 40 percent of the recoverable oil from that reservoir. This is based on a 70 percent recovery of the oil in place which, it was stated, may be 10 percent too low. Two percent of the 1B recoverable oil was produced in 1951, the year of discovery. Reserve figures for sands other than the 1B were not given.

Photo No. 29. Equipment For Handling Flexible Electric Conduit For The Down-Hole Reda Type Pump. Also Note Field Storage Tanks.

Pressure Maintenance

Water flooding for the 1B sand began in 1952, using fresh water from the river. Presently thirteen peripheral wells are introducing twenty percent more fluid than is being withdrawn. By hydrofracing, injection wells are able to take high inputs, as high as 1,000 cubic meters per day.

Transportation

The crude oil goes by pipeline to Stalingrad. From there, it can move by barge either up or down the Volga or down the Don to the Black Sea. A pipeline, to be built by 1965, will move the crude to the Black Sea export base at Tuapse.

Personnel

There are 2,000 people attached to the enterprise, 230 of whom are engineers. Three hundred are social workers, who are engaged in constructing dwellings, community buildings and general community services.

Wages and Hours

The workday was said to be seven hours, the workweek six days. Hours per week are held to forty through a scheduling system. Drillers are paid as much as 3,000 rubles per month; others on drilling crews and those who do comparable production work get about 1,800 rubles per month. Lesser production workers get 1,000 rubles per month, including new technical people in orientation. Social workers are paid 900 rubles per month.

Costs

Production costs, including amortizing drilling costs over twelve to fifteen years, were said to be twelve to fourteen rubles per ton. Other capital items are amortized over twenty-five years. In figuring those costs, only about one-half the total personnel are charged directly against production. Apparently, these extra personnel costs are charged directly against drilling. The cost of fourteen rubles per ton was considered a low figure. In spite of considerable discussion on the point, the delegation was not certain that all costs were included, and was not certain precisely how those included were treated.

Organization

Zhirnovsk production and exploration is handled through a self-contained, local organization, including geologists, engineers, and other technicians. Subdivisions include:

Production (and pressure maintenance)
Drilling
Workover
Power Production
Social Service
Labor
Gathering System

Inclusion of drilling was said to be unusual. As a rule, this would be done by a separate drilling trust responsible to the Stalingrad sovnarkhoz.

D. Offshore Production

1. Azerbaydzhan

Virtually all of the offshore production of crude oil in the USSR has been provided by those fields lying offshore and adjacent to the Apsheron Peninsula of Azerbaydzhan. Major exploitation of these deposits began shortly after the close of World War II and steady increases in production have been maintained since that time. In fact, the growth in production of crude oil in Azerbaydzhan in the postwar years and that planned through 1965 has derived entirely from those increments in offshore production. As a share of total crude output in the republic, that from the offshore fields has increased from 2.4 percent in 1940 to 33 percent in 1959. By 1965, further increases, to 40.5 percent, are planned. Production from the offshore deposits is running well ahead of plan and the goals established for 1965 are expected to be fulfilled in 1961, or 4 years in advance. (See Table 25.)

Table 25

Offshore Production of Crude Oil in the USSR*
Selected Years 1940-65

Year	Amount (Thousand Metric Tons)
1940	534
1948	1,080
1949	1,178
1950	1,571
1951	2,061
1952	2,748
1953	3,239
1954	3,533
1955	4,071
1956	4,411
1959	5,640
1965 Plan	8,910

*All from Azerbaydzhan SSSR.

Available information indicates that the major offshore producing areas of Azerbaydzhan are the following: Artyom or Pirallakhi Island, both on-shore and offshore; Gyurgyany offshore; Banka Darvina; Neftyanyye Kamni; Zhiloy (Ronas Island); and the oil fields of Bukhta imeni Il'icha. Of these, by far the most productive is Neftyanyye Kamni (see Table 26).

Table 26

Offshore Production of Crude Oil in Azerbaydzhan, by Field
1950–55

Thousand Metric Tons

Year	Artyom Oil Administration			Gyurgyan Oil Adm.		Oil Fields Bukhta imeni Il'icha	Total
	Artyom	Gyurgyany Offshore	Banka Darvina	Neftyanyye Kamni	Zhiloy		
1950	644	503	6	–	–	418	1,571
1951	633	852	37	111	12	416	2,061
1952	552	921	99	687	66	423	2,748
1953	473	716	133	1,412	100	415	3,239
1954	427	639	141	1,853	102	371	3,533
1955	432	525	220	2,413	106	375	4,071

The commercial possibility of the extraction of crude on Neftyanyye Kamni (Oil Rocks) was established in 1949 and the working of the deposits began two years later. This deposit rapidly became the leading offshore producer, and its yield in 1955 was almost equivalent to total offshore extraction in the USSR in 1952. Cumulative production of crude oil from the offshore fields covering the period from inception in 1922 and extending through 1955 totalled 35.4 million tons. Of this amount, Neftyanyye Kamni had provided 18.3 percent after having been under exploitation only 5 years.

Neftyanyye Kamni was not visited by the delegation. The history of its discovery and development was shown on film and additional facts were developed by discussion. There were two films, one, "Oil in the Caspian", recording discovery in 1949 and development in the 1950's, the second, "Conquerors of the Sea", a follow-up made in 1959. This second is available in the US. The first, the more interesting, could probably be obtained.

The structure lies some 100 kilometers offshore in the Caspian in the vicinity of shoals and one or two small, low islands. Surface geology extended by offshore seismic work gave the initial picture. The producing section is tertiary, the twenty producing sands lying between 2,400 and 3,000 meters. These sands are being produced from the bottom up, the bottom three each between 15 and 25 meters in thickness, presently being produced as triple completions. Porosity is high, permeability runs from 10 to 1,000 millidarcy, the average being 280. Sand flow is a problem; in one especially thick sand (50 meters) satisfactory production through a plastic squeezed into the formation was described. The type of plastic was not specified.

Although drilling started in 1949, the field is not yet drilled up. Some wells are drilled from separate offshore installations from which several deviated holes are drilled. Most are drilled and serviced from a series of interconnecting causeways supported on piling. The floor is 7 meters above calculated wave height, average water depth is 20 meters. There are now said to be more than 100 kilometers of causeway connecting the wells, tank batteries, living quarters, and so forth.

Oil withdrawn is replaced by injecting Caspian water, the water being injected on one side of the structure, oil being withdrawn on the opposite side between the gas cap and the water. That this is the precise picture is not clear. It may have been an oversimplified explanation. The original reservoir pressure of 350 atmospheres is being maintained. Costs of producing the oil from this field are said to be below costs for comparable features on shore and an 80 percent recovery of oil in place is expected. Using customary Soviet spacing, there must be from 600–800 producing wells in the field.

Most of the exploitation of the offshore deposits is carried out through the construction of so-called "artificial islands", or lengths of steel trestles from which wells are drilled and which also serve as foundations for roadways and workers' quarters. Some of these trestles connect the offshore facilities with the mainland, others are isolated in the open water. The steel supports, which provide the foundation for these trestles, are subject to a high degree of corrosion. Khrushchev, in his visit to Neftyanyye Kamni offshore fields in 1960, took note of this situation and suggested that concrete pilings be used instead. The local administrators regarded this as a true revelation and in early 1961, it was announced from Baku that the first reinforced concrete supports had been built, following the advice of Khrushchev.

Only one floating drilling platform currently is in operation in the Caspian Sea. This platform, similar in design to those in use in the US and built by the Baku Ship Repair Plant of the Caspian Sea Fleet, began initial operations early in 1960. Capable of drilling wells with depths up to 600 meters and operating in sea depths of 2.5 to 6.5 meters, the platform was used in the coastal zone of the Alyatskiy Promontory and in the region of Glinyanyy Island. A total of 22 structural-exploratory wells was drilled in the first year of operation. Construction of another floating platform is now under way. This platform, weighing 500 tons, will be capable of drilling in sea depths of up to 40 meters. Still another platform, weighing 750 tons, and capable of operating in sea depths of up to 100 meters, is being designed.

2. Other

Initial work is under way on the development of the offshore deposits of the Turkmen SSR. These deposits, located on the eastern shore of the Caspian Sea and opposite those of Baku, are concentrated in the area of the Cheleken Peninsula. In addition, some exploratory work has been carried out to the north, in the vicinity of the Mangyshlak Peninsula, but results so far have not been too promising.

Soviet geologists attach great importance to the offshore deposits of the Caspian Sea and are of the opinion that these deposits extend for a distance of some 300 kilometers, linking the eastern and western shores of the Caspian Sea.

E. Costs of Production

The average cost of production of crude oil in the USSR, which also includes the cost of production of associated natural gas, has declined steadily during the period 1950–60, from 57.31 rubles per ton in 1950 to an estimated

30 rubles per ton in 1960 (see Table 27 and Figure 8). Further declines are anticipated during the remaining years of the Seven Year Plan, to about 21.24 rubles per ton by 1965, or the equivalent of 2.93 rubles per barrel. The costs of production of crude oil in the Urals-Volga region are estimated to be about 50 percent of the national average. For individual regions that

Table 27

Reported, Estimated and Planned Costs of Production of Crude Oil and Associated Natural Gas in the USSR
1950, 1955-60 and 1965 Plan

Year	Rubles per Metric Ton	$US per Barrel*
1950	57.31	1.96
1955	46.47	1.59
1956	41.36	1.42
1957	37.27	1.28
1958	34.67	1.19
1959 Estimate	32	1.10
1960 Estimate	30	1.03
1965 Plan	21.24	0.73

*In this calculation, the official ruble-dollar exchange rate of four to one, which prevailed up to January 1, 1961, was used. Some members of the delegation believe that a more nearly accurate exchange rate to be used when converting costs of production from rubles to $US would be 10 to 1. This belief has been based on a ruble-dollar ratio derived from comparing relative costs of drilling in the US and the USSR. If this ratio is applied, then an estimate of the cost of production in 1960 would be about 41 cents per barrel, declining to about 29 cents per barrel by 1965.

comprise the Urals-Volga, the cost of production of crude oil and associated natural gas varies to some degree. For the Tatar ASSR, the cost of production is only 39.6 percent of the national average, for Kuybyshev Oblast — 42.1 percent, and for the Bashkir ASSR — 53.7 percent of the national average. Conversely, costs of production in areas outside the Urals-Volga significantly exceed the national average, as shown in the following:

Area	1958 Cost of Production of Crude Oil and Associated Natural Gas (National Average - 100)
Ukraine SSR	153
Turkmen SSR	165
Azerbaydzhan SSR	217
Sakhalin Island	331

The lowest costs of production of crude oil in the USSR are found at the Mukhanovo fields in the Kuybyshev Oblast. The cost of production per ton of crude oil from these fields averages about 10.2 rubles (the equivalent of 35¢ per barrel at the exchange rate of 4 rubles per $US 1, or 14¢ per barrel at an exchange rate of 10-1). Data for other individual oil fields indicate that Romashkino crude averages about 18.4 rubles per ton and that Tuymazy crude averages about 22.4 rubles per ton.

Authoritative Soviet sources indicate that the predrilling costs of core drilling and geophysics and the investment in exploratory drilling are not

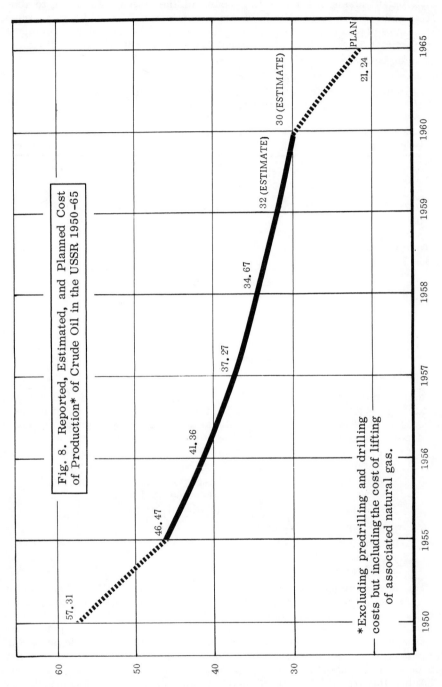

Fig. 8. Reported, Estimated, and Planned Cost of Production* of Crude Oil in the USSR 1950–65

*Excluding predrilling and drilling costs but including the cost of lifting of associated natural gas.

reflected in the reported costs of production. If an exploratory well yields crude (or gas) then this well is given the same cost as an analogous development well.

Soviet planners recognize the necessity for revising the basis for calculation of production costs, so that the geological-exploratory expenses will be included, thus to bring cost and price closer together. According to 1957 data, the return to the State from even the most profitable oil fields was not sufficient to cover the exploratory investment. It has been pointed out by one Soviet writer that inclusion of the exploratory costs in the costs of production of crude oil would not necessitate an increase in petroleum product prices paid by the consumer. It would mean, however, that the wholesale prices of the products would increase. To defer an increase in retail prices, this writer suggested a reduction in the turnover tax, a portion of which is used to finance the exploratory expenses in any case.

The structure of the reported costs of production of crude oil and associated natural gas in the USSR for 1958 was as follows:

	Percent of total
Energy expenditures	7.1
Wages	6.5
Amortization of wells (15-year period) and other fixed assets	42.0
Current repairs	9.3
Increasing of strata yield	9.8
De-emulsification of the crude	2.6
Field collection, transport and storage of crude	4.6
Collection and transport of the associated natural gas	2.6
Office expenditures	6.5
General oil field expenditures	9.0
Total	100.0

For all of the petroleum-producing regions of the country, the amortization of wells and other fixed assets represents the major share in the cost structure. Wider use of water flooding has resulted in continued annual increases in the share attributed to increasing of the strata yield; for the Tatar ASSR, 21.4 percent of the cost of production of the crude is represented by the cost of water flooding.

On the other hand, the water flooding program results in a higher portion of the annual production of crude oil being provided by free-flowing wells. In turn, this results in a reduced cost of production, for the cost of producing crude from free-flowing wells averages about one-sixth of the cost of crude from deep-pump wells.

Although costs of production for the USSR on the average have declined since 1950, as shown in Table 27, those costs in certain of the oil-producing regions for 1958 show an increase over 1950. In Azerbaydzhan, costs of production in 1958 were 11 percent above 1950 costs; costs in the Turkmen SSR were about 2.5 percent above 1950 costs.

Because the desire to meet the annual goal for production apparently dominates most of the thinking, Soviet oil experts miss an opportunity for reductions in the costs of production. The annual goal is distributed among the various producing fields in an enterprise. To meet this goal, all of the production available is needed, which precludes the opportunity to shut down the more expensive wells.

F. Methods of Production and Means for Increases

During the 10-year period 1950-60 the share of crude oil which has been extracted from the free-flowing wells in the USSR has increased from 32.5 percent of the total national production to 74 percent of the total. This increase has been at the expense of production from wells equipped with pumps and from wells using the so-called compressor method; i.e., gas or air lift. The distribution of production of crude oil in the USSR, according to method of production, for selected years 1946-60, and 1965 plan is shown in Table 28.

Table 28

Methods of Production of Crude Oil in the USSR
1946, 1950, 1955-60 and 1965 Plan
(As Percent of Total)

Year	Free-Flowing	Pump	Compressor*	Other	Total
1946	20.3	43.0	36.0	0.7	100
1950	32.5	44.7	21.1	1.7	100
1955	58.3	34.0	6.5	1.2	100
1956	64.8	29.4	5.0	1.0	100
1957	69.0	26.5	3.9	0.6	100
1958	70.4	25.6	3.4	0.6	100
1959	72.7	24.2	2.6	0.5	100
1960	74.0	23.5	2.0	0.5	100
1965 Plan	72.5	26.3	1.2	0	100

*Gas or air lift.

1. Water Flooding

The increase in the share of crude oil provided by free-flowing wells has largely been the result of initiation and successful fulfillment of a program of water injection. The injection of water into oil-bearing formations in the USSR is begun at the initial period of development of the field in question. Only those deposits which are commercially insignificant or which have powerful natural water drives are excluded from this program.

The basic approach has been that of peripheral water drive. This method has been used successfully at most of the oil fields of the Urals-Volga. However, at some fields a combination of peripheral and intra-contour water flooding has been applied. In this approach, injection wells are drilled not only along the periphery but also in the intra-contour oil bearing deposit, thus cutting the deposit into separate fields, each to be developed independently.

Probably the most notable application of the combination of peripheral and intra-contour water flooding has been at the Romashkino oil field in the Tatar ASSR, reportedly the largest not only in the Soviet Union, but in the world. A thorough analysis of the economics of development of this major oil field indicated that exploitation through application of peripheral water flooding alone would take 250 years. Under these conditions the maximum annual level of extraction would not exceed 7 million tons and the cost of production per ton would be significantly greater than under the combined method. Therefore it was decided to divide the deposit through the drilling of intra-contour injection wells into 22 independent fields, thus reducing the duration of exploitation to 30-50 years, but allowing a significant increase in the annual level of production. Of the ultimate 22 independent fields, 7 are already in operation.

The annual yield of crude oil from the program of water flooding has increased from 3.4 million tons in 1951 to 45 million tons in 1960. Significantly, it has been these yields which have been primarily responsible for the sharp growths in annual production of crude oil in the USSR during the postwar period. In the prewar period the major share of production of crude oil from new wells served only to cover the drop in production from old wells. For example, the growth in production of crude oil in 1940 was only 900,000 tons, yet the production of crude oil from new wells had reached 5.5 million tons; thus 4.6 million tons were needed to offset the decline in production from old wells. In contrast, the production of crude oil from new wells in 1956 was reported at 9.3 million tons, but the increment in production in that year totalled 12.9 million tons. This apparent decline in the relative importance of new crude oil has derived from the successful program of water flooding.

At present, the deposits which are included in the water flooding program account for 63 percent of the national production of crude oil. Furthermore, it is claimed that up to 70 percent of the oil in place is being recovered. By 1965, 81 percent of the national crude output is to be provided by deposits where water flooding is employed.

The volumes of water injection and the resultant crude oil yield for the years 1950-60 are shown in Table 29.

Table 29

Effect of Water Injection at Oil Fields of the USSR

1951-57, 1960, and 1965 Plan

Year	Daily Water Injection (Cubic Meters)	Annual Crude Oil Yield (Thousand Metric Tons)
1951	42,755	3,359
1952	70,560	4,770
1953	126,769	7,621
1954	189,336	11,618
1955	252,749	16,245
1956	312,752	19,387
1957	348,818	23,805
1960	612,000 (Plan)	45,000
1965 Plan	850,000	na

Research on oil displacement by other means is continuing. Considerable interest has been given to the possible use of liquefied gases (propane). It is claimed that this method will allow the recovery of up to 90 percent to 95 percent of the oil in place. Experiments with thermal drive also have received attention.

2. Hydraulic Fracturing

It was indicated to the delegation that hydraulic fracturing was used primarily for improving injectivity of water wells rather than for increasing the productivity of producing wells. The results obtained in the application of hydraulic fracturing as a means for increasing crude oil yield have been somewhat less than desirable. As explained one Soviet authority, the usefulness of hydraulic fracturing had not been fully accepted and efforts had been hampered by inadequate equipment and financing.

Photo No. 30. Hydraulic Fracturing of Strata at the Ekhabi Oil Fields
on Sakhalin Island.

The most effective use of hydraulic fracturing operations has been achieved in Azerbaydzhan. During the years 1954–58 and including the first six months of 1959, a total of 3,035 hydraulic fracturing operations had been carried out in this area. Of these operations, 52.3 percent were effective, resulting in an additional production of 485 thousand tons of crude oil. Data on hydraulic fracturing of strata covering all of the USSR during 1955–60 is shown in the following tabulation:

Year	Number of Operations	Crude Oil Yield (Thousand Metric Tons)
1955	878	178.4
1956	1,901	346.0
1957	2,905	na
1958	2,713	na
1959	2,262	na
1960 Plan	3,000	1,000.0

It should be noted that one of the highlights of the visit of the Soviet oil delegation to the US in October–November, 1960, was the opportunity for these experts to observe a hydraulic fracturing operation at Spraberry, in

West Texas. Furthermore, the first reporting in the Soviet press of the oil delegation was limited to photographs and text covering the Spraberry operation.

3. Acidizing

Minor use is also made of acidizing of producing formations, again primarily in Azerbaydzhan. The number of acidizing operatings in Azerbaydzhan increased from 91 in 1952, which yielded an additional 7,500 tons of crude oil, to 1,190 in 1958, yielding 133,100 tons. Despite the relatively low return, a total of 31,000 such operations for the USSR as a whole has been planned for 1959-65.

4. Automation in Production

Persistent questioning at the various institutes revealed that the USSR evaluates labor-saving devices much as any company in the US does, comparing in this the payout versus wages. Most automation in the oil fields, it was reported, gave a three-year payout, but labor-saving equipment would be installed if it paid out in seven years or less.

The program for automation in the field is barely under way. Of the total of 32,000 wells under exploitation in 1959, only 2,000 had been placed under automatic control. By 1965, however, about 70 percent of all active wells are to be under automation and telecontrol. As companion to the automation of production, most of the pumping stations connected with water flooding are to be automatically controlled.

Present collection systems are semi-automatic. Because the field attendants were not interested in precise accounting, flow meters are seldom used to measure the flow. Instead, the strokes of the booster pumps are measured remotely to determine the producing rate of a well. At Tuymazy each well in addition to the separator had a small storage tank. It was the impression of at least one of the delegation that the production was metered by counting the number of tankfuls produced.

G. Estimate for 1965

It is estimated that the production of crude oil in the USSR in 1965 may reach as much as 265 million tons. This estimate represents a compromise between earlier estimates and estimates obtained during the visit of the Soviet oil delegation to the US during October-November, 1960. These latter estimates ranged from 250 million tons, attributed to the head of the Soviet delegation, to as much as 288 million tons, expressed privately by other members of the delegation. Achievement of this projected level of production would represent a major overfulfillment of the goal of 240 million tons established by Soviet planners for 1965.

As shown in the tabulation below, achievement of a level of production of 265 million tons of crude oil in 1965 would call for only an extension of the general trend in the growth of the absolute annual increments established since 1955. A major, upward deviation from this trend, which would be necessary to achieve any considerably higher production level, is not anticipated nor is it reflected in any of the Soviet plans covering the remaining years of the Seven year Plan.

Considerable publicity has been given recently to the achievement of the goals of the Seven Year Plan in 6 years. The following timetable allows for this achievement, in that production in 1964 is estimated at 236 million tons,

Year	Production (million tons)	Increment (million tons)
1955	70.8	–
1956	83.8	13.0
1957	98.3	14.5
1958	113.2	14.9
1959	129.6	16.4
1960	147.9	18.3
1961 Plan	164.0	16.1
1961 Est.	167.0	19.0
1962 Est.	188.0	21.0
1963 Est.	211.0	23.0
1964 Est.	236.0	25.0
1965 Est.	265.0	29.0*

*A growth of 4 million tons in the absolute annual increment is anticipated for 1965, in light of the probable push in the last year of the Seven Year Plan.

which falls midway within the range of 230-240 million tons which was announced in 1958 in the Seven Year Plan thesis as the goal for 1965. Later, Soviet publications carried 240 million tons as the plan for 1965.

H. Proved Reserves

Although the delegation was not provided with a definitive statement concerning the measure of proved reserves of crude oil in the USSR, references were made on several occasions to the fact that the USSR currently was producing its reserves at a rate of 4 percent to 5 percent a year for the larger fields. It was also suggested that the smaller fields were being produced at the rate of 10 percent per year.

It is estimated that the proved reserves of crude oil in the USSR at the beginning of the Seven Year Plan reached 2.5 billion metric tons. These reserves reportedly are to increase 1.7 times during 1959-65, thus to total 4.25 billion tons on January 1, 1966. The larger portion of these reserves, approximately 80 percent, are concentrated in the Urals-Volga. Those in Azerbaydzhan at present average 4 percent to 5 percent of the national total and are to remain at this level through 1965. Estimates of proved reserves of crude oil in the USSR for selected years 1930-60 and 1965 plan are given in Table 30.

Table 30

Estimated Proved Reserves of Crude Oil in the USSR
by Selected Area, at End of Year
1936, 1950, 1958, 1960 and 1965 Plan

Area	Million Metric Tons				
	1936	1950	1958	1960	1965 Plan
Azerbaydzhan	570	n.a.	125	135	250
Urals-Volga	35	530	1,990	2,600	3,400
Other	280	n.a.	385	515	600
Total	885	800	2,500	3,250	4,350

Much more meaningful than these data, however, is the recognition of the vast area of the Soviet Union which is considered geologically suitable for the occurrence of crude oil and natural gas. This area measures some 11 million square kilometers, exceeding that of the US by more than 60 percent. Much of this area has yet to be explored. It suffices to say that the resources are more than adequate to support any reasonable crude oil production program.

XI. REFINING

A. General

The four refineries which the delegation visited — Novo-Ufa, Novo-Kuybyshev, Novo-Baku, and Syzran' — represented about 26 percent of total refinery capacity available in the USSR. It is believed that these refineries are representative of that capacity constructed prior to the beginning of the Seven Year Plan in 1959, and may be compared to those refineries in existence in the US following World War Two. With the exception of Syzran', which was built in 1942 but which has undergone considerable expansion since 1946, these refineries were constructed between 1951 and 1956. It is probable that the general comments on these refineries are applicable to the entire industry.

For the output of fuel products, a typical processing scheme includes desalters, atmospheric and vacuum distillation units, Thermofor catalytic cracking, thermal cracking of residual, gas recovery and butylene alkylation. In the manufacturing of lube oil, propane deasphalting, phenol treating, solvent dewaxing and clay treatment is employed. No catalytic reforming was seen in any refinery other than one prewar fixed bed molybdenum oxide catalyst unit at Novo-Ufa. There are no hydrogen treating units in operation. At Novo-Kuybyshev, it was claimed that a catalytic reforming unit was under construction and would be in operation in 1961, but there was no opportunity to visit the construction site. The 1965 goal is 5 million tons per year of catalytic reforming. Discussion with refinery personnel revealed that some difficulty was being encountered in the elimination of hydrogen attack in their reformers. Catalytic reforming will not be used to improve gasoline quality directly, but as a source of chemical raw materials. It will help balance supplies of gasoline and distillates.

The refineries visited were characterized by extremely poor construction, maintenance and housekeeping standards. Much of the equipment lacked paint. The insulation and weatherproofing were disintegrating and steam leaks from valves and gaskets were abundant. In the insulation of a hot line, the first step was to wire on a brick measuring 4'' x 6'', followed by plaster over the brick. Product piping is laid in concrete trenches about one to two feet deep, then covered with concrete slabs about 18'' wide, 3 feet long, and 3'' thick. These irregular slabs had two lifting hooks at either end. This method results in a very irregular trench covering which presents a considerable safety hazard. At the Syzran' refinery, the trenches had been filled with sand as a safety precaution.

Almost all of the control houses had broken windows and in a heavy rain leakage around the windows and through the roof joints was clearly evident. Some of the control houses had curtains at the window and were decorated with large house plants.

Many simplex and duplex reciprocating pumps were used. Brass valves were used on the pumpout lines from the pumps — even on those pumps in hot service. Nearly all of the pumps were steam driven and some plants were venting large quantities of excess steam. The control instruments were all air actuated. Virtually all of the plants were equipped with the large scale old type recorders and controls. There was no explosion-proof equipment in the control houses.

The fire protection at these refineries was well below US standards. There were a few hand extinguishers in evidence and no high pressure water or fixed foam systems. None of the supporting steel structures were insulated for fire. Boxes of sand and shovels were located around the units and in the laboratories. It was stated that fires were fought with steam, CO_2 and portable foam. However, there was no indication of fire damage in the refineries visited.

Safety standards paralled those of fire protection. The workers do not wear hard hats except when inside a chamber doing repair work, nor were hard toe safety shoes worn. There were no goggles or safety showers at the sulfuric acid alkylation units. The absence of these protective measures, combined with low piping, uneven stairways, irregular covered trenches and uneven steel floor plates on the structure, would be expected to result in a high accident incidence. Nevertheless, it was claimed that the safety record was satisfactory.

The refineries are spaciously laid out. There is a normal allowance of 100 meters between gas units, 200 meters between units and storage, and 40 meters between other units. It appeared that most of these standards were exceeded, thus adding to the capital and operational costs incurred by the wide spacing.

The average size of process units was small considering the capacity of a refinery. Standard designs and sizes have been established and multiple units are used where required. An average crude unit has an annual charge capacity of 1.5 million tons. Thermofor catalytic cracking units charge about 500,000 tons. Standard sizes apparently are being increased. Most of the new refineries under construction utilize the new standard of 6 million ton charge capacity, using either two or three crude units. This scheme would include one new size Thermofor catalytic cracking unit of about 1.25 million ton capacity.

Refinery design institutes have developed standardized types of refining process schemes depending on the type of crude available. Crude oils are divided into 3 general categories, with a process arrangement for each:

Type I — Crude Oil under 1.9 percent sulfur (producing both fuels and lubes) — Atmospheric and Vacuum Primary Distillation; Thermal Cracking; Catalytic Cracking; Catalytic Reforming; Lube Oil Production; Asphalt Production (from lube plant).

Type II — Crude Oil under 1.9 percent sulfur (fuels only) — Atmospheric and Vacuum Primary Distillation; Thermal Cracking; Catalytic Cracking; Catalytic Reforming.

Type III — Crude Oil over 2.0 percent sulfur — Atmospheric distillation.

B. Yields

Although the four refineries which the delegation visited were not particularly impressive, it must be admitted that all were running and performing their functions adequately. The finished products, although crude by US standards, had a waiting market. There is no competition and no demand for high quality products which must be met. Product quality need be only as high as what is considered to be practical.

The major problem confronting the Soviet refining industry, one that was freely admitted, is the continuing high content of sulfur in the crude oil. The sulfur content of the average Soviet crude is increasing as output from the older fields declines and as new discoveries are put into production. In 1951, less than 33 percent of the crude had a sulfur content of from 0.5 percent to 1.9 percent, but by 1959 this share had increased to 62 percent. Of the remainder, 18 percent had a sulfur content of up to 0.5 percent and 20 percent of total national production of crude contained more than 2 percent sulfur. Increases in the output of the highly sulfurous crude oil in the Urals-Volga, particularly in the Bashkir ASSR, where in 1965 two-thirds of the crude will contain more than 1.5 percent sulfur, including more than 42 percent with a sulfur content above 2.5 percent, will significantly raise the share of sulfurous crude oil in the total volume of crude charged to refining. This share is to reach as much as 75 percent by 1965, including 15 percent of highly-sulfurous crude. Currently, average sulfur content appears to be about 1.5 percent.

Another problem, of only slightly less import, is an imbalance in the production and demand for gasoline and for diesel fuel. Present refinery capabilities yield a production of gasoline beyond those quantities required for the domestic market. On the other hand, the output of diesel fuel is said to fall short of demand. To alleviate this situation, a portion of the gasoline is consumed as a diesel fuel, some diesel fuel is produced at below-standard specifications, and some diesel engines are supplied with a mixture of automobile gasoline and diesel fuel. It is planned to increase the production of gasoline engines to bring about a better balance.

Soviet refineries in 1959 ran about 20 percent gasoline and about 23 percent diesel fuel. For 1965, a slight decline has been planned in the percentage yield of diesel fuel, but a sharp decline in the share of gasoline to less than 16 percent of the total output. Most of the relative declines in gasoline and diesel fuel output is to be made up in increased yields of residual fuel oil.

Probable yields by product type for 1959 and 1965 are shown in Table 31.

Table 31
Estimated Output of Petroleum Products in the USSR by Type of Product
1959 and 1965 Plan

Type of Product	1959		1965 Plan	
	Million Metric Tons	Percent of Total	Million Metric Tons	Percent of Total
Gasoline	24	20.3	35	16.4
Kerosine	15	12.7	24	11.2
Diesel Fuel	27	22.9	43	20.1
Lubricants	5	4.2	8	3.7
Residuals and others	38	32.2	87	40.7
Total	109	92.0	197	92.0
Gas and Loss	9	8.0	17	8.0
Grand Total	118	100.0	214	100.0

The reader is cautioned that while these yields may very nearly represent the domestic demand for such products in 1965, the internal consumption of a specific product or products can and has been suppressed as other needs, say foreign trade, of the economy take precedence.

Considerable effort is to be made to raise the octane number of the automobile gasoline. In 1958, of the total production of automobile gasoline, 25 percent had an octane rating (motor method) between 56-60. This share was to have declined to 20 percent in 1959, and further in 1960 to 5 percent. The plan for automobile gasoline octane ratings in 1959 envisaged the following distribution:

Octane rating (Motor Method Clear)	Percent Total Production
72 and above	2.2
70	2.5
66	75.2
56-60	20.1

Beginning in 1962, the output of 70-octane gasoline in Azerbaydzhan is to be discontinued, and with the planned additional capacity for catalytic cracking, only 72-octane gasoline is to be produced. For the USSR as a whole, the output of 72-octane and higher gasoline in 1965 is to exceed 40 percent of the total volume of production of gasoline, while the share of 66-octane gasoline has been placed at 58.6 percent.

Because of low temperatures in the USSR, diesel fuel pour points are said to be critical because of the high paraffin content of some crudes. Diesel fuel pour points are +14° F summer and -13 to -22° F winter. It is planned to use a new Urea Adduct process for paraffin removal to improve the pour points.

An example of the degree of rigidity of specifications for petroleum products is given in Table 32, which presents specifications for the jet fuels T-1, TS-1, T-2 and T-5.

C. Capacity and New Construction

There has been a noticeable trend in the postwar years in the USSR to allocate the available capital investment, labor, equipment and material to the greatest number of projects possible within a single industry. As a result of this program, in the petroleum industry a great number of refineries have been under simultaneous construction and the annual capacity brought on stream has been much less than if effort had been concentrated at fewer sites. In addition, much of the refinery design became obsolescent even before completion.

Only recently, however, the responsible Soviet authorities have taken note of this shortcoming and a concentration of effort at fewer sites has been called for. Apparently, it is hoped to complete those refineries whose construction stages are relatively advanced and to withhold further committment on those just started until the prior objective has been reached.

There is no single geographic concentration of construction on new refining capacity. New capacity is being installed in Siberia as well as in the highly populated and developed area surrounding Moscow. Included among those refineries which are to benefit from an acceleration of construction are the following: Ryazan', Stalingrad, Perm', Omsk, Angarsk, Novo-Yaro-

Table 32

Specifications for Soviet Jet Fuels
Grades T-1, TS-1, T-2, and T-5

Specification	Grades			
	T-1* (GOST 4138-49)	TS-1** (GOST 7149-54)	T-2*** (GOST 8410-57)	T-5+ (GOST 9145-59)
Density, 20°/4°(68°/39°)++	0.800–0.850	0.775 (min)	0.755 (min)	0.845 (min)
Distillation, °C (°F)				
IBP	150 (302) (max)	150 (max)	60 (140) (min)	195 (min)
10% (max)	175 (347)	165 (329)	145 (293)	225
50% (max)	225 (436)	195 (383)	195	not specified
90% (max)	270 (518)	230 (446)	250 (482)	not specified
98% (max)	280 (536)	250	280	315 (599)
Residue and loss, % (max)	2	2	2	2
Vapor pressure, psi	not specified	not specified	1.3 (max)	not specified
Kinematic Viscosity, Centistokes				
At 20° (68) (min)	1.5	1.25	1.05	5.0
At 0° (32) (max)	4	2.5	not specified	not specified
At -40° (-40) (max)	16	8.0	6.0	60
At -50° (-58) (max)	25	not specified	not specified	not specified
Acidity, mg of KOH/100 ml (max)	1.0	1.0	1.0	1.0
Flash point (closed cup), °C (°F) (min)	30 (86)	28 (82)	not specified	not specified
Freezing point, °C (°F) (max)	-60 (-76)	-60	-60	-60
Cloud point, °C (°F) (max)	-50 (-58)	-50	not specified	not specified
Iodine No., gm/100 gm (max)	2	3.5	3.5	3
Aromatic content, % (max)	25	22	22	22
Gum content, mg/100 ml (max)				
a. At refinery	8	7	7	8
b. At point of consumption	11	10	10	11

Table 32 (continued)

Specifications for Soviet Jet Fuels
Grades T-1, TS-1, T-2, and T-5

Specification	Grades			
	T-1 (GOST 4138-49)	TS-1 (GOST 7149-54)	T-2 (GOST 8410-57)	T-5 (GOST 9145-59)
Sulfur, wt. % (max)	0.1	0.25	0.25	0.1
Mercaptan sulfur, wt. % (max)	not specified	0.01	0.01	not specified
Water soluble acids and alkalies	none	none	none	none
Heat of combustion, Kcal/kg (min)	10,250	10,250	10,250	10,250
Ash content, % (max)	0.005	0.005	0.005	0.005
Mechanical impurities and water	none	none	none	none
Copper strip corrosion test	not specified	must pass	must pass	must pass
Thermal stability				
a. In LSA-1 unit 150°C for 1 hour (mg/100 ml)	not specified	not specified	not specified	no firm specified but test must be run
b. In bomb 150 for 4 hours (mg/100 ml)	not specified	not specified	not specified	no firm specified but test must be run

* Produced by straight run distillation of low sulfur crude oils.

** Produced by straight run distillation of high sulfur crude oils.

*** Produced by straight run distillation of low or high sulfur crude oils.

+ Produced by straight run distillation, probably from low sulfur crude oils.

++ Temperatures in °F appear in parentheses throughout this table.

slavl', and Fergana. The geographic dispersal of facilities is the result of planning to bring the centers of refining of crude oil closer to the centers of consumption. The culmination of this program will represent the second major shift in principal location of refining capacity that has taken place in the USSR during the history of the petroleum industry (see Table 33).

Table 33

Shift in the Center of Oil Refining in the USSR
Selected Years, 1933-55
(In percent of total refining charge)

Region	1933	1940	1946	1950	1955
Caucasus (Azerbaydzhan, Groznyy and Krasnodar Kray)	81.5	80.3	66.0	55.8	36.5
Urals-Volga and Central	1.8	8.1	21.7	30.1	44.5
Other*	16.7	11.6	12.3	14.1	19.0
Total	100.0	100.0	100.0	100.0	100.0

*Primarily in Central Asia.

The first such change followed the shift in the center of production of crude oil away from Baku and to the Urals-Volga area. Gradually in the postwar years, lesser prominence has been given to Baku, until by 1955, the whole of the Caucasus contained only 36.5 percent of total national refining capacity.

The second change reflects the gradual settlement and industrial development of other areas of the USSR, particularly to the east of the Ural mountains, in addition to increased demand in the European Russia. Some inequity remains in the Urals-Volga region, however. The Soviet press carries a continual complaint to the effect that the Tatar ASSR, a leading producer of crude oil, has no refining industry, and that all of the crude must be shipped out and products imported from other areas of the country.

An increase of approximately 130 million tons of primary refining capacity is planned during 1959-65. Although planned additions to primary refining capacity during 1959-65 exceed planned additions to secondary refining capacity, the percentage increases in secondary refining capacity will be about double the percentage increase in primary refining capacity. Estimated primary and secondary refining capacity in the USSR for 1958, 1959 and 1965 is as follows (in millions of tons):

Process	1958	1959	1965
Primary	120	140	250
Secondary	40	60	130

Distribution of the refinery throughout capacity for 1959 according to refinery is given in Table 34.

According to plan, the desired increment in refining capacity to be achieved during 1959-65 is to be furnished as follows: 37 percent from those refineries already under construction; about 20 percent through reconstruction and expansion of existing capacity; about 23 percent through intensification and partial reconstruction of existing technological units; and 20 percent through those refineries, the construction of which was to begin after 1959.

Table 34

Estimated Refinery Throughput Capacities of the USSR
1959

Refinery or Complex Capacity* (Million Metric Tons)	Refinery
21	Baku complex
18	Kuybyshev complex
	Ufa complex
14	Omsk
10	Groznyy complex
7	Syzran'
	Krasnovodsk
6	Ishimbay/Salavat
5	Gur'yev
3	Gor'kiy complex
	Saratov
	Tuapse
	Tuapse
	Moscow
	Fergana
	Perm'
	Stalingrad
2	Batumi
	Orsk
	Vannovskaya
1	Krasnodar

* The refineries listed in this table account for 134 million tons of the total of 140 million tons of capacity available in the USSR at the end of 1959. The remaining six million tons is to be found largely in the following refineries: Ukhta, Drogobych, L'vov, Mukhachevo, Chop, Kherson, Staro-Yaroslavl', Novo-Yaroslavl', Konstanti- novskiy, Tbilisi, Krasnokamsk, Kim, Komsomolsk, Khabarovsk, and Odessa.

Thus, about 43 percent of the new capacity for refining of crude oil planned for 1959-65 is to come from the reconstruction, expansion and intensifica- tion of use of existing refineries and units. Primary refinery capability was only barely adequate for processing the crude charge in 1959. The maximum capability to utilize annual installed primary capacity in the USSR is be- lieved to be only 80 percent to 85 percent. Thus, primary refinery facilities are believed to have been capable of handling not more than about 120 mil- lion tons of crude oil in 1959, which very nearly equals that amount charged.

If it is assumed that in 1965, approximately 85 percent of the installed primary capacity will be utilized, then charge to refineries in that year would approach 212 million tons. This estimated charge of 212 million tons, which probably would yield about 198 million tons of products, thus would be more than sufficient to meet the probable domestic demand of 187.5 million tons in that year and would in part provide for the export of certain petroleum products.

An increase of 90 million tons in capacity for secondary refining is planned for 1959-65. This increase primarily reflects the desire to achieve better quality and a better product mix from the low-quality crude of the

Urals-Volga. There has been a general deterioration in petroleum product quality in the USSR. This deterioration may be attributed to a lack of capacities for catalytic secondary refining and to the high sulfur and paraffin content of the crude oil charged to refining. To raise the quality levels, the USSR must increase the capacities of processes such as cracking, reforming, and hydrotreating. Included in the original Seven Year Plan were the objectives of increasing capacity for catalytic cracking by 4.3 times and for catalytic reforming by 16 to 18 times.

D. Notes on Refineries Visited by Delegation

1. NOVO-UFIMSKY (NEW UFA) REFINERY

This refinery is located near Ufa, capital of the Bashkir ASSR, about 1,130 kilometers east of Moscow. Construction of the plant began in 1949 and it was placed in operation in 1951 with a capacity of 7.5 million tons per year. It was further expanded starting in 1953 and by 1956 had been increased to the present 11.5 million tons per year level. The actual crude run in 1959 was 10.7 million tons. This is the only plant for which an actual crude run figure was available. Based on these figures the apparent stream efficiency is 93 percent. The plant was stated to have cost 1.5 billion rubles. Crude oil is received by pipeline from the Bashkiria and Tataria regions. There is an old Ufa refinery with a capacity of 6 million tons per year nearby which was not visited by the delegation. An additional new refinery of 12 million tons per year is under construction.

The refinery property is about 3 by 7 kilometers in area. Process units are very widely spaced, possibly for safety. Like all refineries in the USSR, capacity of storage tanks is very low by US standards. Under their planned economy this is feasible since practically all products are always in short supply. There can be no surplus as long as even minimum product demands are not being met.

There is a town with a population of about 200,000, approximately 10 kilometers from the refinery. The usual facilities, such as apartment buildings, hospitals, palace of culture, and the like are provided for the workers at this location. Transportation is provided by street railway and buses for movement to the plant and to the central part of Ufa which is considerably further. The refinery furnishes services, including gas, electricity, and water as well as labor for the town. There is quite an industrial complex in the Ufa area which includes production of minerals, chemical plants, smelting, and fabrication of machinery and electrical goods.

Total personnel employed is 5,000, including 320 town maintenance employees and 600 engineers or technicians. Women are 45 percent of the total. Operations personnel is 60 percent and administrative or clerical is 4 percent of the total.

Apparently, all Soviet refining units are scheduled for definite run and turnaround periods. At this plant we were given some definite schedules for these. Crude units are scheduled for 8-12 month runs, apparently averaging 24 days down per year. Thermal cracking units are shut down for 5 days every 50 days for preventive maintenance and 15-20 days yearly for capital maintenance. Catalytic cracking units are shut down for 8 days every 150 days and 22-25 days each 2 years for capital maintenance.

The fairly high, and increasing, sulfur content of the crude oils processed has led to the use of alloy materials containing chromium, nickel and molybdenum. Alkaline neutralization with lime, caustic soda and soda ash is also necessary to combat hydrochloric acid corrosion.

In this plant, as in others which were visited subsequently, little attention seems to be paid to safety but, nevertheless, the Russians point with pride to their record. Hard hats were reported to be available but were not required and none were observed. No safety shoes were seen. There were 18 lost-time accidents at this refinery during 1959. Most of these were burns at the thermal cracking units. Time lost varied from 3 days to 1-1/2 months away from the job.

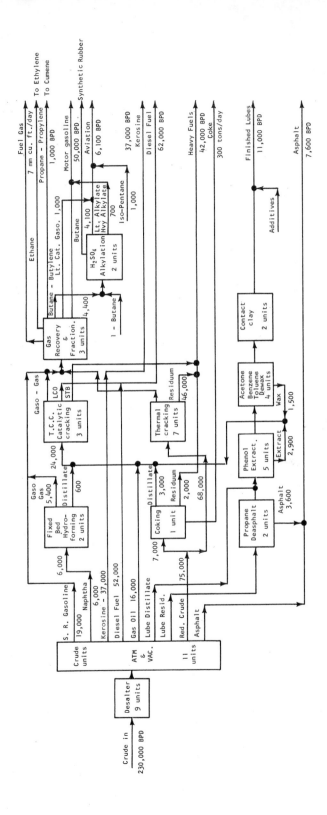

Fig. 9 NOVO-UFA REFINERY

OPERATING UNIT DATA:

Crude Units - 230,000 BPD*
    Number of Units - 11
    Typical Unit Built 1955
    Nominal Capacity - 220,000 BPD
    Actual Operation - 24/26,000 BPD
    Type - Atmospheric and Vacuum - Conventional
    Atmospheric Column - 11.5 ft. diameter - 30 trays
    Vacuum Column - 21.5 ft. diameter - 14 trays
Thermal Cracking Units - 700,000 BPD
    Number of Units - 7
    Type - Conventional
Delayed Coking Unit - 7,000 BPD
    Number of Units - 1 (called experimental)
    Three Chambers - Hydraulic Decoking
    Coke Chamber Capacity - 300 cubic meters each - 100 tons
    Production: Overhead Stock - to Catalytic Cracking
                Heavy Distillate - to Fuel
                Coke - 4% Sulfur - to Sale
Fixed Bed Hydroforming - 6,000 BPD
    Number of Units - 2
    Typical Unit Built 1954
    Type - U.S. Wartime Design
    Catalyst - Molybdenum Oxide
    Reactors - 4 on 6-7 hour cycles, 2 in parallel
    Gasoline Charge - 44 MON
    Product - 76-76 M
    Product - 72-76 MON
    Pressure - 295 Lbs. - Temperature - 1020° F.
    Regeneration - Inert gas containing 1.5% oxygen circulated by turbo-
        compressor.
Catalytic Cracking - 24,000 BPD
    Number of Units - 3
    Typical Unit Built 1953
    Type - Thermofor with dual airlifts. Side by side.
    Charge - Gas oils and coker distillate.
        390° - 850° F. for Aviation Gasoline
        9000 BPD - Fresh Feed
    Recycle - 20% of Fresh Feed
    Catalyst - Silica-Alumina Bead
    Oil to Reactor - 895° F.
    Average Reactor Temperature - 842° F.
    Regenerator Temperature - 1250° F. Max.
    Catalyst Circulation - 110 Tons, U.S. per hour
    Five operators per shift

---

*For purposes of easier comparison with US counterparts the operating
data and flow sheet data for this refinery and others visited by the delegation have been put into the English system.

Yield - Weight %: Gas 14-16
                    Gasoline 25-30
                    Syn Tower Bottoms - 5.0
                    Coke - 4.6

Sulfuric Acid Alkylation - 6,400 BPD
  Number of Units - 2
  Typical Plant Built 1952
  Nominal Capacity - 2,700 BPD total alkylate
      85% Light Alkylate - 5.8# RVP
      15% Heavy Alkylate
  Outside Iso-Butane-Olefin Ratio - 6-7
  Stratford Type Reactor
  Reactor Temperature - 32 -68°F. Ammonia cooling
  Acid Consumption - 0.8-1/3#/bbl. alkylate
  Final Treatment - Caustic Wash @ 100°F.
  Seven operators per shift

De-Salting Units - 250,000 BPD
  Number of Units - 9
  Typical Unit Built 1953
  Nominal Capacity - 26/30,000 BPD
  Type - Electrical and Chemical - 12 vertical drums
  Salt Content In - 1050-1750 lbs./1000 bbls.
  Salt Content Out - 17.5 lbs./1000 bbls.

Lubricating Oil Facilities
  Propane De-Asphalting - 5000 BPD
  Number of Units - 2
  Phenol Extraction - 15,500 BPD
  Number of Units - 5
  Typical Unit Built 1953
  Nominal Capacity - 2,600/3,000 BPD
  Contractor - 8.5 ft. diameter x 72 ft. high
  Raschig ring packing. Some perforated plates also used.
  Phenol Inlet - Top of column.
  Acetone-Benzene-Toluene Dewaxing - 12,500 BPD
  Number of Units - 4
  Type - Ammonia-Ethane Cooled - 2 stage
  Lowest Filtering Temperature - 76°F.
  Drum Type filters, belted cotton cloth with beryllium bronze wire sup-
    port. Life of cloth - 6 months.
  Filter Rates - 4.4 gal/hr./sq. ft. (stock for this rate not designated)
  Wax is not suitable for candle wax.
  Contact Clay Filtration - 11,000 BPD
  Number of Units - 2

Gas Recovery and Fractionation - 56,000 BPD
  Number of Units - 3
  Typical Unit Built 1952
  Absorber Pressure - 175 lbs.
  Stripper Temperature - 660°F.
  Absorption Oil - Kerosine
  Stabilizer
    Charge: Light cracked gasoline
                Catalytic stabilizer reflux
                Absorption gasoline

Products: Ethane to Ethylene Plant
            Propane to Cumene Plant
            B–B to Alkylation (includes 150 TPD IC$_4$)

Refinery Charge and Yield Data (Estimated)

Crude Units

Charge - Crude Oil, 33° API - 2.0% S - 2.0% BS & W   230,000 BPD

Products	Volume %	BPD
S.R. Gasoline	8.2	19,000
Reformer Charge	2.8	6,000
Kerosine & Jet Fuel	15.9	37,000
Diesel Fuel	22.5	52,000
Lube Plant Charge	8.3	19,000
Asphalt	1.9	4,000
Gas Oil - Cat Cracking	6.8	16,000
Reduced Crude	32.6	75,000
Gas & Loss	1.0	2,000

Lube Plant Operations

Charge - Lube Distillate & Residuum -   19,000 BPD

Products	Volume %	BPD
Asphalt	19	3,600
Extract - Cat Cracking	15	2,900
Wax - Cat Cracking	8	1,500
Finished Lubes	58	11,000

    Finished Lubes Average   85 V.I.
    Additives Bring Up To   95 V.I.

Fixed Bed Hydroformer

Charge - 44 MON -   6,000 BPD

Products	L.V. %	BPD
Reformate - 76-6 O.N.	80	5,000
Distillate - Cat Cracking	10	600
Gas to Gas Plant	10	

Coking Unit

Charge - Reduced Crude -   7,000 BPD

Products	L.V. %	BPD
Light Distillate - Cat Cracking	43	3,000
Heavy Distillate - Fuel Oil	28	2,000
Coke		300 Tons
Gas	10% Weight	

Catalytic Cracking

Charge - Gas Oil and Distillate -   24,000 BPD

Products	L.V. %	BPD
Gas to Gas Plant	15% Weight	
Gasoline	30	7,200
Light Cycle Oil	40	10,000
Syn Tower Bottoms - Fuel Oil	14	3,000
Coke	5% Weight	15,700 lb./hr.

Thermal Cracking

Charge - Reduced Crude   68,000 BPD

Products	L.V. %	BPD
Gas	7% Weight	
Gasoline	29	19,000
Fuel Oil	67	46,000

Alkylation Unit			BPD	
Charge:				
Refinery Butenes			2,800	
Refinery Iso-Butane			1,600	
Outside Iso-Butane			2,000	
Total Charge			6,400	
Products				
Light Alkylate			4,100	
Heavy Alkylate			700	
Propylene to Outside Chemical Plant for				
Cumene			1,000	

Consolidated Yields			BPD	
Charge:				
Crude Oil - .86 Sp. Gr. - 2% S			230,000	
Iso-Pentane			1,000	
Iso-Butane			2,000	
Products	Wt. %	Vol. %	BPD	
*Gasoline	20	23.9	56,000	
Kerosine-Jet Fuel	15	15.9	37,000	
Diesel Fuel	27	27.0	62,000	
Asphalt	4	3.5	8,000	
Lube Oils	5	4.8	11,000	
Fuel and Gas	27	23.5	52,000	
Loss	1	1.4		
Coke	1			300 Tons
Propylene		0.4	1,000	

*Includes 1,000 BPD iso-pentane blended into aviation
    Motor Gasoline   Total - 50,000 BPD
    Aviation Gasoline   Total - 6,100 BPD

2. NOVO-BAKU REFINERY

This refinery, completed in 1953, charges 3 million tons per year of 29 API crude oil from the Baku, Karadag and Artyom regions. The present Seven Year Plan calls for its capacity to be doubled. Sulfur content of the crude is normally low but may at times run as high as 1-1/2 percent. It will average between 0.5 percent and 0.7 percent. No lubricating oils are produced. Crude oil is received through a 10-inch pipeline which continues to Batumi, a Black Sea port. Products are shipped from the refinery through two pipelines and by rail. One pipeline is parallel to the crude oil line to Batumi. The other product line extends to a marine loading terminal on the Caspian Sea.

The refinery includes a plant for manufacturing bead catalyst. Catalyst for the Fluid cracking units is reported to be fines from the TCC units. It has a laboratory divided into two sections — one of which serves for Process Control while the other provides Process Engineering services. The plant generates most of its own power but some is supplied from outside.

This refinery has a higher ratio of catalytic cracking to crude capacity than most Soviet refineries. If the catalytic cracking is not increased as the crude capacity is enlarged under the Seven Year plan, it will approach the average ratio. The total personnel employed are 2,000 of which 180 are in "town" service. There are 200 engineers and 100 technicians. Twenty-nine percent of the employees are women, most of whom work in the laboratories and catalyst plant. There is a sustaining community adjacent to the refinery complete with homes, apartments, hospital, recreation center, and kindergarten.

Photo No. 31. Desalting Unit and Pipe Still at Novo-Baku Refinery.

General Process Scheme:
Crude as received by pipeline is desalted and charged to the crude units. They are a two-column design with no vacuum step. Products are straight run gasoline from the first column and kerosine, diesel fuel and gas oil catalytic cracking charge from the second. Bottoms from the second column are reduced crude for thermal cracking charge.

Light fractions from catalytic cracking except for butenes and isobutane are sent to outside petrochemical plants. The ethane-propane fraction goes to an outside synthetic alcohol plant. The butylenes are alkylated for production for light and heavy alkylate. Normal butane is sent outside where butadiene is produced in a two-step dehydrogenation. It is copolymerized with styrene for synthetic rubber. Part of the amylenes are used in an outside operation producing alkyl aryl sulfonates.

OPERATING UNIT DATA:

Desalting Units - 60,000 BPD
    Number of Units - 2 (similar to units at New Ufa)
                12 precipitators
                crude heated by exchange
                water injected
                settled
                second wash injected
                dehydrated
Plans call for addition of 4 dehydrator tanks per unit.
Charge: 140-175#/1000 bbls. salt.
Product: 5-7#/1000 bbls. salt.

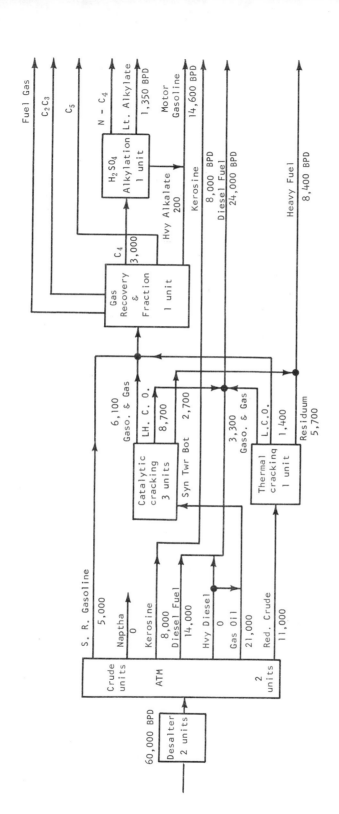

Fig. 10 NOVO-BAKU REFINERY

Crude Units - 60,000 BPD
   Number of Units - 2
   Typical Unit: 2 column atmospheric
                    overhead of first column - gasoline
                    side stream "naphtha"
                    overhead of second column - kerosine
                    side stream "gas oil"
                    2 coil heater
                    #1 coil reboils first column
                    #2 coil preheats charge to second column
                    Condensers are of submerged coil type using Caspi-
                    an Sea water (0.5% salt)
   Charge: 29° API crude sulfur 0.5%

		Wt. %
Products:	Gasoline	7
	Illuminating kerosine	13
	Distillate fuel oil	26
	Resid (Mazut)	52
	Gas and loss	2

Thermal Cracking - 11,000 BPD
   Number of Units - 1
   Charge: Residuum

		Wt. %
Products:	Gas and loss	7
	Gasoline	25
	Tractor Fuel	7
	Residual Fuel	51
	Distillate fuel oil	10

Catalytic Cracking - 21,000 BPD
   Number of Units - 3   Thermofor - 2, Fluid - 1
                    Gas Oil IBP 435°F. - 92-95% @ 662°F.
                        EP 680°F.

		Wt. %
Products:	Wet Gas	15-16
	Gasoline	25-26
	Diesel Fuel	30
	Heavy Diesel Fuel	13-15

   Catalyst Type - Silica-Alumina
Gasoline from catalytic cracking is treated for gum removal by passing through a silica-alumina catalyst. Possibly a re-treat for aviation grade only.

Thermofor (Moving Bed) Catalytic Cracking
   Typical Unit - Capacity 7,000 BPD Fresh Feed plus 15% Recycle.
   Catalyst Type - Bead
      Reactor and regenerator are side by side with two air lifts to surge separators feeding the vessels. Total height of unit - 263 feet.
   Reactor: Downflow - Vapor and Catalyst
      Size - 16 feet diameter
      Feed - 100% vapor @ 895 °F.
      Catalyst Inlet Distributors - 28
      Catalyst Draw-off Pipes - 16
   Reactor Temperature - 860° F.
      Reactor Pressure - 7.3 lbs./sq. in.

Recycle Charge - 15% of fresh feed
Regenerator:
    Size - Square - 10 feet across
    Burning Zones - 8
    Cooling Coils - Generate - 175 lb./sq. in. steam
    Carbon Burn - 2,200 lbs. per hr.
    Catalyst Circulation - 110 tons per hr.
    Carbon on Spent Catalyst - 1.5-1.6% wt.
    Carbon on Regen. Catalyst - 0.5-0.15% wt.
    Maximum Regenerator Temperature - 1,260° F.
    Regeneration Air Supply - Heat Turbine (Possibly gas turbine)
    Regeneration Air Temperature - 660° F.
    Lift Air Temperature - 660° F.
    Catalyst Loss - 3 tons per day

Fluid Catalytic Cracking

Catalyst Type - Silica-Alumina (Said to be fines from Thermofor Units)
Regenerator and Reactor side by side except regenerator is 100 feet above reactor. Described as Model II.
Typical Unit - Capacity 7,000 BPD plus 25% Recycle.
Reactor: Diameter - 16 feet
        Height - 52 feet
        Temperature - 842-896° F.
        Pressure - 7.3 lbs./sq. in.
Cat/Oil Ratio - 5-6:1
Catalyst Hold-up - 0.7 (average)
Reactor Grid - Plate with 2 in. orifices
Regenerator: Diameter - 26 feet
          Height - 52 feet
          Temperature - 1075-1110° F.
          Pressure - 1.5 lbs./sq. in.
Cyclone - external
Regeneration Air - Apparently 6 injection points, spaced vertically.
Regeneration Control - Catalyst color comparisons.

Alkylation - 1550 BPD - Alkylate

Type - Stratford Sulfuric Acid
Charge - Thermal and Catalytic B-B Cut
Ratio of Iso-Butane to Olefin - 1.3
Ratio of Iso-Butane to Olefin in Reactor - 5.5
Fresh Acid Strength - 98%
Spent Acid Strength - 84% Ois used for treating)
Acid/Hydrocarbon Ratio - 0.8-1.3
Reactor Temperature - 46-59° F. (ammonia refrigeration)
Reactor effluent alkali washed before fractionation.
Product is 88% light alkylate for aviation gasoline.

Gas Plant

Columns - 5 in series, bottoms of each flowing to next.

Absorber

Main gas inlet under 10th tray.
Gasoline absorption oil admitted on 13th tray.
Depentanized gasoline refluxed to 40th tray.
40 trays - 205 lbs. per sq. in. pressure.
Temperature - 86-95° F.

Photo No. 33. Thermofor Cat Cracker at the Novo-Baku Refinery.

Photo No. 32. Fluid Cat Cracker at the Novo-Baku Refinery.

Compressors – 2-stage angle type gas engine.
   First Stage Pressure – 58 lbs./sq. in.
   Second Stage Pressure – 235 lbs./sq. in.

Desorber
  Steam reboiled
  Temperature – 104-158° F.
  Pressure – 177 lbs./sq. in.
  Overhead Product – C_2 to chemical plant for alcohol production.
  Bottoms – Pumped to depropanizer

Depropanizer
  Temperature – 293-302° F.
  Pressure – 250 lbs./sq. in.
  Overhead Product – C_3 fraction to chemical industry for pyrolysis to
   ethylene then to ethanol to butadiene.
  Bottoms to debutanizer.

Debutanizer
  Pressure – 90-100 lbs./sq. in.
  Overhead product to alkylation.
  Bottoms to depentanizer.

Depentanizer
  Overhead amylene and iso-pentane to outside chemical industry for
  production of alkyl aryl sulfonates.

Refinery Charge and Yield Data

Crude Unit – 2 units
  Charge – .875 sp. gr. – 0.5% S   60,000 BPD

T/D	Sp.gr.	Products	Wt. %	L.V. %	BPD
575	.74	Gasoline	7	8.3	5,000
1,070	.81	Kerosine	13	14.0	8,000
1,840	.865	Diesel	23	23.3	14,000
3,000	.88	Gas Oil to Cat Cr.	36	35.0	21,000
1,640	.94	Residuum to T.Cr.	20	18.4	11,000
82		Loss	1	1.0	

Thermal Cracking – 1 unit
  Charge – .94 sp. gr.

	Charge	Wt. %	L.V. %	BPD
	Reduced Crude	100	100	11,000
	Products			
.76	Gasoline	24	29.7	3,300
.875	Distillate	12	12.9	1,400
1.02	Residuum	57	52.0	5,700
.94	Gas and Loss	7	5.4	

Catalytic Cracking – 3 units

.88	Charge	Wt. %	L.V. %	BPD
	Gas Oil	100	100	21,000
	Products			
	Gas, C_5 & Ltr.	15	20.0	4,200
.76	Gasoline	25	28.9	6,100
.90	Light Cycle Oil	30	29.3	6,100
.92	Heavy Cycle Oil	13	12.4	2,600
1.00	Syn Tower Bottoms	14.5	12.8	2,700
	Coke	2.5		158 M lbs.

Alkylation Unit - 1 unit

Charge		BPD
n-Butane, Iso-Butane, Butenes		3,000
Products		
n-Butane		1,000
Light Alkylate		1,350
Heavy Alkylate		200

Consolidated Yields

Charge		60,000
Crude Oil - .875 sp. gr. - 2% S		
Products	Vol. %	
Gasoline	26.7	16,000
Kerosine	13.3	8,000
Diesel Fuel	35.8	21,500
Heavy Diesel	4.3	2,600
Heavy Fuel	14.0	8,400
Loss and Gas	5.8	3,500

Photo No. 34. View of Novo-Baku Refinery.

3. SYZRAN' REFINERY

This refinery was placed in operation in 1942. It charges 7 million tons per year of 35° API Urals-Volga crude oils. The crude oil averages 1.5 percent with maximum of 2.0 percent sulfur. It is the only refinery visited which does not have a catalytic cracking unit. A Thermofor unit is under construction.

It receives its crude oil by pipeline and river barge. Products are shipped by rail, barge and pipeline except paving asphalt which is shipped by truck.

The refinery has and maintains housing for employees, totalling about 47,000 square meters. Each person is allotted about 7.5-8.5 square meters of living area. Certain employees are allowed private housing with an allowance to assist in purchase. There are some 22,000 square meters of

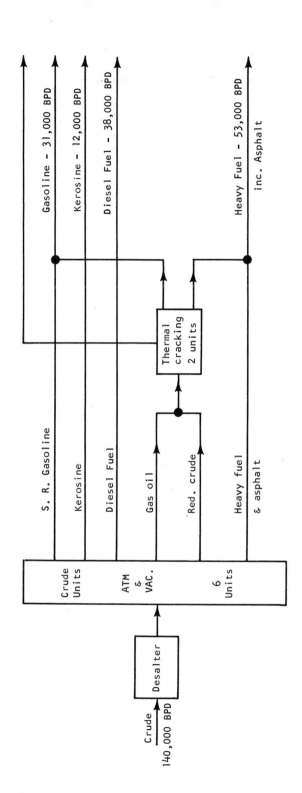

Fig. 11 SYZRAN REFINERY

this type housing. The State provides utilities for both types, including water, gas, electricity, and roads. In 1959, 750,000 rubles were allowed as a credit for private housing.

The process scheme for this refinery is confused since we are not sure how many units of each type are in service. We do not have yield data except on an over-all basis. It is, however, run primarily for fuel oils. Some illuminating kerosine is produced but scheduled amounts have been reduced every year for the past five years.

There are 1,600 employees of which 170 are in "town" service. Also included are 150 engineering personnel. Forty-five percent are women. The work week is 36 hours for shift work and 40 hours for others. The plant earned a bonus of 1.5 million rubles for exceeding its goals in 1959. The total cost of the plant was 203 million rubles.

OPERATING UNIT DATA:

		BPD
Crude Units - 6 - 140,000		
2 Atmospheric Vacuum		40,000
2 Atmospheric Vacuum		12-14,000
1 Atmospheric Topping		12-14,000
1 Combination Unit		20,000

(Built in 1958. Is similar to U.S. combination units.)
Thermal Cracking - 2 units - 54,000 BPD
    Typical Unit - Capacity 27,000 BPD
    Two Coil: Once through visbreaking
                Light oil recycle cracking
    Under Construction: 1 - Thermofor Catalytic Cracking Unit
                        1 - Thermal Cracking Unit

Composite Yields - Estimated			BPD
Charge - Crude Oil - 35° API			140,000
Products	Wt. %	L.V. %	
Gasoline	19	22	31,000
Kerosine	8	8.5	12,000
Diesel Fuel	28	27	38,000
Heavy Fuel & Gas	43	38	53,000
Loss	2	4.5	6,000

Product Quality
    Gasoline - 66 Motor Method with 3 ml/gal. TEL
                74 Research Octane
        3 ml/gallon is apparently legal limit for TEL.
    Diesel Fuel - 50 Cetane
                Flash 104° F. to 149° F. (seasonal)
                % S - 0.2 to 1.0

4. NOVO-KUYBYSHEV REFINERY

This refinery was built after World War II and started operation in 1951. It charges 15 million tons per year of 34° API crude from the Urals-Volga basin. This oil has a sulfur content up to 2.0 percent but generally ranges around 1-1/2 percent. The oil is similar to that charged to the Novo-Ufa refinery. As part of the Seven Year Plan, it is planned to increase the capacity of this refinery to twice its present size as far as light product production is concerned. No expansion of lubricating oil facilities is contemplated. Products are shipped from the refinery by barge, rail, pipeline, and truck.

Photo No. 35. Interior View of Novo-Kuybyshev Refinery.

Crude is desalted and dehydrated by chemical and electrical equipment similar to that in the other refineries visited. It is charged to 10 crude units and streams are taken to catalytic cracking, thermal cracking, and lube oil manufacturing facilities. Intermediate storage is provided for blending gasoline and diesel oils.

Light products from the cracking units are processed in an alkylation unit or sent to outside chemical plants. No jet fuel is produced. A catalytic reformer is said to be under construction and will be placed in operation early in 1961. Two additional units are planned. There is a good-sized city for employees adjacent to the refinery. It includes apartments, two hospitals, a clinic, and technical school.

Total personnel employed are 4,500, including about 180 engineers and 270 technicians. Thirty-five percent of the employees are women. The number of employees does not include social workers.

OPERATING UNIT DATA:

Desalting Units - 300,000 BPD
  Number of Units - 10
  Typical Unit - 12 vertical drums
  Capacity - 30,000 BPD
  Operating Voltage - 30-32 K.V.

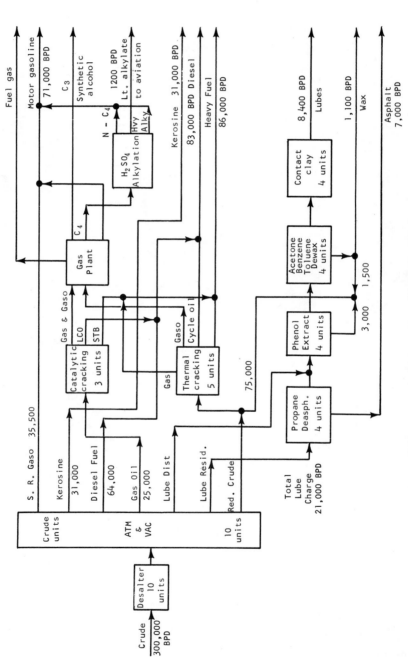

Fig. 12 NOVO-KUYBYSHEV REFINERY

Product - Contains 7-14#/1000 barrels salt
Two additional units using spheres are under construction.

Crude Units - 300,000 BPD

Number of Units - 10
Size of units vary from 29,000 to 40,000 barrels per stream day.
Four of the units have a vacuum stage.
Main Crude Tower Diameter 12 ft. - 24 trays.
Vacuum Tower Diameter - 16.5 ft.
Operating pressure 1 in. Hg Abs.
Temperatures kept low to prevent damage to lube stock.
Reduced crude from vacuum stills is charged to propane deasphalting.

Thermal Cracking Units - 75,000 BPD

Number of Units - 5
Typical Unit - 15,000 BPD
Reported "Cracking Temperature" - 1008° F.—1022° F.

Catalytic Cracking Units - 25,000 BPD

Number of Units - 3 (additional unit under construction)
Type - Thermofor with dual air lifts
Fresh Feed Rate - 8,500-9,000 BPD plus 25% recycle

Normal Gas Oil Charge:		High Octane Charge:	
IBP	482-518°F.	IBP	392-428°F.
25-30%	662° F.	50%	662°F.
EP	887-932°F.	EP	824°F.

Some light charge is included to prevent catalyst damage by excessive coke formation. Coke is carefully controlled.
Catalyst Type - Silica alumina bead

Reactor: Downflow - vapor and catalyst

Diameter - 13 feet
Bed Depth - 23 feet
Temperature - 869-878° F.
Pressure - 7.3-8.0 lbs./sq. in.
Catalyst Circulation - 90 tons/hr. (100 U.S. tons)

Regenerator:

Diameter - 11.5 feet (square)
Burning Zones - 9
Carbon Burning Capacity - 4,400 lbs. per hour
Maximum Temperature - 1320° F.
Normal Temperature - 1080° -1180° F.
Carbon on Spent Catalyst - 2.7-2.8% wt.
Carbon on Regen. Catalyst - 0.4% wt.

Alkylation Unit - 1,200 BPD

Number of Units - 1
Hydrogen sulfide is recovered for outside sulfur manufacture using monoethanolamine
Sulfuric acid alkylation charging refinery B-B

Lube Oil Operations

Propane Deasphalting Unit - 21,000 BPD

Number of Units - 4
Typical Unit - 5,500 BPD
Operating Pressure - 590#/sq. in.
Charge: Vacuum residuum
    Raffinate yield - 35%
    Raffinate to phenol extraction

Phenol Extraction Unit
 Number of Units - 4
 Typical Unit - Capacity 3,300 BPD distillate or
                          3,300 BPD deasphalted stock
 Yield - 78% on distillate
         70% on deasphalted stock
         Phenol use .03#'s/barrel
 Note: Previously phenol use has ranged from 0.6 to 0.1#'s per barrel
   of charge.

Acetone-Benzene-Toluene Unit - Dewaxing
 Number of Units - 4
 Typical Plant - 2 stage ammonia refrigeration, ethane for very low
          pour.
 Oil Yield - 80%
 Wax Quality - Oil content 1.0-1.5% wt.
 Special Grade - 0.7% wt.
 Note: All lubricants are finished by contact filtration.

Product Properties
 Gasoline
 Regular Grade   - 72-74 F-2 O.N.
 Premium Grade   - 83-87 F-2 O.N.
 Maximum Lead Content   - 3 ml/gal.
 Tractor Fuel
 Octane Number   - 40° F-2 O.N. min.
 Illuminating Kerosine
 Regular   - 22-24 m.m. flame height (smoke point)
 Premium   - 25-30 m.m. flame height (smoke point)
 Diesel Fuels
 Sulfur Content   - 0.2 - 1.0%
 Pour Points   - Summer
                                   - Winter
 Flash (Closed Cup)   - 167° F.
 Lubricating Oils
 V.I.   - 90-95 Some 100
 Waxes   - 122/126° F. MP
                                     143/147 F. MP
 Heavy Fuels
 Kinematic viscosity of grades 40, 60, 80, 100 and 200.
 Saybolt Furol @ 122° F., approx. 25, 30, 37, 50 and 100.
 Asphalts
 Grade BN 3   Softening Point   - 113-122°F.
                     Penetration   - 20 25 min.
                     Ductility   - 40 cm. min.
                     Softening Point   - 176-212°F.

Refinery Charge and Yield Data				BPD
Crude and Vacuum Units - 10 Units				300,000
Sp.gr.	Products	Wt. %	Vol. %	
.70	S.R. Gasoline	9.7	11.8	35,500
.80	Kerosine	9.6	10.3	31,000
.84	Diesel Fuel	20.9	21.3	64,000
.885	Cat Cracker C	8.7	8.4	25,000
.90	Thermal Cracker Chg.	24.7	23.5	70,500

Sp.Gr.	Products	Wt. %	Vol. %	BPD
.90	Lube Plant Charge	7.4	7.4	21,000
.92	Heavy Fuel	18.0	16.7	50,000
.855	Loss	1.0	1.0	3,000
		100.0	100.0	300,000

Lube Plant Operations - 4 Units

Charge				21,000

Products			L.V. %	
Finished Lubes			40.0	8,400
Asphalt			33.0	7,000
Phenol Extract to Thermal Cracking			14.0	3,000
Slop Wax to Thermal Cracking			7.0	1,500
Wax			5.0	1,100

Catalytic Cracking Operations - 3 Units

Sp.Gr.	Products	Wt. %	Vol. %	
.885	Charge			25,000
	Gas to Plant	14.0	–	–
.76	Gasoline	30.0	34.0	8,500
.90	Light Cycle Oil	33.7	32.0	8,000
.96	Heavy Fuel	18.0	17.0	4,200
	Coke	4.3	17.0	168 Tons/Day

Thermal Cracking - 5 Units

Sp.Gr.	Products	Wt. %	Vol. %	BPD
	Charge			75,000
.76	Gasoline	30.0	35.5	27,000
.875	Distillate	15.0	15.4	11,500
1.00	Residuum	47.0	42.3	32,000
	Gas & Loss	8.0		

Alkylation - 1 Unit

Charge				3,000
Products				
Light Alkylate				1,200
Heavy Alkylate				200
n-Butane				1,000

Consolidated Yields

Products	Wt. %	Vol. %	
Charge - .855 sp.gr. 34°API - 1.5% S Crude			300,000
Gasoline	20.2	23.6	71,000
Alkylate	0.3	0.4	1,200
Kerosine	9.6	10.3	31,000
Diesel Fuel	27.8	27.6	83,000
Heavy Fuel	32.0	28.6	86,000
Asphalt		2.3	7,000
Wax		0.4	1,100
Lube Oils		2.8	8,400
C₃ Fraction ⎱ n-Butane ⎰		1.0	3,000
Gas & Loss	1.8	2.7	8,300

XII. CONSUMPTION

A. Current

Most of the output of petroleum products in the USSR is directed to fuel industry, to service the agricultural tractor and combine park, and to meet the requirements of military and civil aviation and the large number of trucks in daily use. Very little remains for use as a household fuel or in non-essential consumption. As shown in Table 35, in 1959 an estimated 45 percent of total national consumption of petroleum products was attributed to industry. The military forces of the USSR, including the Civil Air fleet, accounted for about one-sixth of the total, which ranks this sector as the third largest consumer of petroleum products. Significant amounts were consumed in agriculture and transport activities, reaching 20 percent and 16 percent respectively. The use of petroleum products for heating and cooking by the so-called communal-household sector, which includes consumers such as apartments, restaurants and the like, reached only 2.2 million tons in 1959 or 2.3 percent of total national consumption.

Estimates of consumption by type of product for 1955 and 1959 are given in Tables 36 and 37. The more complete estimates for 1955 given an

Table 35

Estimated Consumption of Petroleum Products in the USSR
by Consuming Sector
1955 and 1959

Consuming Sector	1955		1959	
	Million Metric Tons	Percent of Total	Million Metric Tons	Percent of Total
Industry	22.4	38.6	42.8	45.0
Agriculture	11.9	20.4	19.0	20.0
Transport	14.6	25.1	15.2	16.0
Communal-Household	1.6	2.8	2.2	2.3
Total	50.5	86.9	59.2	83.3
Military* and Others	9.0	13.1	15.8	16.7
Grand Total	59.5	100.0	95.0	100.0

*Includes consumption by the Civil Air fleet.

indication of the range of yield of the Soviet refining industry. According to Soviet authorities, some difficulty is encountered in equating the supply and demand for gasoline and for diesel fuel. For the past several years, there has been an apparent surplus of gasoline and a concomitant shortage of diesel fuel. One of the major problems confronting the refining industry is the necessity for an increase in the yield of diesel fuel to meet the growing requirements for this fuel by agriculture and transport. Analysis of trade data for 1959 shows, however, that the USSR in that year was a net exporter of diesel fuel to the extent of 4.3 million tons. On the other hand,

Table 36

Consumption of Petroleum Products in the USSR, by Type of Product
1955

Type of Product	Amount (Million Metric Tons)
Gasoline	
Motor	12.8
Aviation	1.8
Total	14.6
Kerosine	
Tractor	3.0
Lamp and stove, plus jet fuel	
for military use	6.1
Total	9.1
Diesel Fuel	
Light	11.4
Heavy	3.8
Total Diesel Fuel	15.2
Total light products	38.9
Lubricants	2.4
Residuals and others	
Residual fuel oil	16.0
Petroleum bitumen	1.9
Coke	0.1
Other	0.2
Total Residuals and others	18.2
Grand Total	59.5

Table 37

Apparent Consumption of Petroleum Products in the USSR
by Type of Product
1959

Type of Product	Amount* (Million Metric Tons)
Gasoline	23.6
Kerosine	14.4
Diesel Fuel	22.7
Lubricants	4.8
Residuals and others	33.9
Total	99.4

* Production plus imports minus exports, losses and increments to storage.

net exports of gasoline totalled only 0.4 million tons. Because of the
relatively low average octane number of Soviet gasoline, some difficulty
is found in placing this product in the international market. It would appear
from these trade data that under certain circumstances the internal needs
for petroleum products have been given only second priority.

Photo No. 36. Filling Station in the City of Balashov, located in Saratov Oblast. This
city, with a population of 64,000, has 2 filling stations of general purpose, one of which is open all night, the other only half a day. These
stations serve on the average 1,000 vehicles — automobiles and trucks
— each day, selling gasoline, oil and oil filters. Plans for expansion
of one of these stations this year call for the installation of an air
compressor for tires and a water hose. In addition oil and greases
will be sold in packaged form.

Only a comparatively few automobiles, perhaps no more than 500,000,
are in use in the USSR. The contrast in marketing facilities in the USSR
compared to those in the US, which serve the daily needs of more than 60
million automobiles, is extremely great. The delegation observed only
6 filling stations in its travels within the USSR, and these were located
on side streets not readily accessible to the flow of traffic.

B. Prospects for 1965

It is estimated that the consumption, both civil and military, of petroleum
products in the USSR in 1965 may reach 187.5 million tons. The percentage
distribution of this quantity among the various consuming sectors of the
economy approximates that distribution which prevailed in 1959, except
for slight increases in the shares for industry and transport. To effect
these increases, it is anticipated that the share of the military will decline by more than one-third, despite a continuing absolute growth. The
decline in consumption of petroleum by the military sector, attributed to
the substitution of rocket and missile forces for conventional military
weapons and the expanding use of nuclear-powered vessels, has been
softened to some extent through the greater probable use of kerosine by
the jet aircraft of the Civil Air fleet. Distribution of the estimated consumption for 1965 among the various sectors is shown in Table 38.

Much has been made by Soviet authorities of the planned dieselization
of the railroads and of transport in general during the Seven Year Plan.
These authorities point out that the resultant increase in consumption of
petroleum fuels will not make likely any sizeable increase in exports
during 1959-65. While it is true that a major portion of the railroad system
is to be dieselized and that by 1965 diesel locomotives are to perform
almost 45 percent of the total volume of work done, compared with less
than 11 percent in 1958, the consumption of petroleum products by the
railroads in 1965 will not be significant. This is shown in the following

Table 38

Estimated Consumption of Petroleum Products in the USSR
by Consuming Sector
1965

Consuming Sector	Million Metric Tons	Percent of Total
Industry	90	48. 0
Agriculture	38	20. 0
Transport	36	19. 0
Communal-Household	4	2. 1
Total	168	89. 1
Military* and Other	19. 5	10. 9
Grand Total	187. 5	100. 0

* Includes consumption by the Civil Air fleet.

tabulation, which presents the consumption of fuel by railroads in 1958 and
that planned for 1965 (in millions of tons):

Type of Fuel	1958	1965
Coal	94	21
Diesel fuel	1. 165	6. 15
Residual fuel oil	3. 9	7. 3

The widespread introduction of diesel engines in the river and sea
fleets during the years 1959-65 will serve to increase the consumption of
diesel and motor fuel by these sectors from 900,000 tons in 1958 to 3
million tons in 1965. The use of residual fuel oil by these consumers is to
increase during the same period from 1.6 million tons to 2.7 million tons.

The increased availability of natural gas in 1965 will reduce to an un-
known degree the consumption of petroleum fuels by industry, and to a
lesser extent, by the communal-household sector. For example, the electric
power industry, which is a leading consumer of petroleum fuels, is expected to consume more than 26 percent of the total output of natural gas
in 1965. While the consumption of residual fuel oil is to increase from
5.5 million tons in 1958 to 24 million tons by 1965, natural gas is to supply
more energy to this industry than oil. The metallurgical industry (see
Table 39), on the other hand, will reduce its consumption of residual fuel
oil during 1959-65, from 5.1 million tons to 3.6 million tons, as the consumption of natural gas increases from 1.568 billion cubic meters to 27.5
billion cubic meters. Estimates of the distribution of consumption of natural
gas among the various consumers for 1965 are given in Table 40.

Only a slight growth in the consumption of kerosine and residual fuel
oil by the communal-household sector during 1959-65 is planned. Again,
the major influence will be the increased deliveries of natural gas to this
sector. Petroleum products are to provide about 3 percent of the total
consumption of fuel by the city communal-everyday sector in 1965 whereas
natural gas is to provide 20.4 percent, a marked contrast compared with
1958, when natural gas provided only a 7.3 percent share.

Table 39

Consumption of Residual Fuel Oil in the USSR by Consumer*
1958 and 1965

Consumer	Million Metric Tons	
	1958	1965
Metallurgical industry	5.1	3.6
Electric power stations	5.5	24.0
Sea and river fleets	1.6	2.7
Railroads	3.9	7.3
Technological needs of enterprises of the petroleum industry	3.2	5.5
Cement production	0.4	2.0
Sugar production	0.6	2.8
Output of heat in industrial boilers	0.6	3.4
Other branches of industry and other needs	6.4	10.7
Total	27.3	62.0

* Does not include the consumption of residual fuel oil for so-called non-productive
exploitational needs nor its use as a raw material.

Table 40

Estimated Consumption of Natural Gas in the USSR
1965

Consumer	Billion Cubic Meters	Percent of Total
Communal-Household	14.4	9.6
As a Chemical Raw Material and in the Production of Carbon Black	8.5	6.7
By Gas Pipeline and in the Field	11.5	7.7
Industry		
Iron and Steel	27.5	18.3
Non-ferrous	10.8	7.2
Machine-construction	12.0	8.0
Cement	8.4	5.6
Electric Power	39.8	26.5
Railroads	1.0	0.7
Other	16.1	10.7
Total	115.6	77.0
Grand Total	150.0	100.0

C. 1972-75

In late 1959 the Central Economic Scientific and Research Institute (TsENII) of Gosplan, USSR, published a long-range examination of the probable demand for petroleum products in the USSR. This study carried through the years 1972-75. Applying certain of the relations given in this study permits at least a preliminary analysis of the supply and demand for petroleum products in the USSR for that period.

Within the distribution of consumption of petroleum products among the various consuming sectors of the country, no significant change is expected from the pattern anticipated for 1965, with the exception of a decline in the share of agriculture and a concomitant increase in the share for transport.

Table 41

Possible Consumption of Petroleum Products in the USSR
by Consuming Sector (as percent of total), 1975

Consuming Sector	Share
Industry	47.4
Agriculture	16.2
Transport	22.2
Military, Household-Communal and other*	14.2
Total	100.0

* Calculated as a residual.

According to this study, the domestic demand for petroleum products in the USSR during 1972-75 will have increased by 91 percent, compared with the demand in 1965. Accepting this growth yields a possible domestic demand of 360-365 million tons by 1972-75.

It is possible that the production of crude oil in the USSR may reach to as much as 400 million tons by 1970, if the estimate of 265 million tons for 1965 is attained and if a continuation of annual increases in the production of crude oil beyond that level is considered desirable. Thus the production of crude oil in the USSR may be as high as 450 million tons by 1972 which, when compared with possible domestic demand of 360-365 million tons calculated for 1972-75, underscores the probability of continued increases in the surplus of crude oil available for export from the USSR.

XIII. TRANSPORT OF PETROLEUM IN THE USSR

The pattern of movement of oil freight in the USSR presents a sharp departure from that pattern prevailing in the US. Outstanding in this contrast is the highly-developed trunk pipeline system constructed by American enterprises to ensure delivery of crude oil and petroleum products to the consumer by the most rapid, economic and dependable means. On the other hand, the construction of a trunk pipeline system in the USSR has progressed very slowly and the major responsibility for transport of oil freight has been given to an already overburdened railway system (see Tables 42, 43 and 44). In addition, the transport of oil freight by tank truck in the USSR is so insignificant that such data are lost in the official statistics. A partial offset to the latter is the rather intensive use of water transport which, although subject to seasonal limitation, provides the USSR with a supplemental economic means of transport.

The data presented in Table 44 illustrate the dependence of the USSR upon the railroad system for the transport of crude oil and petroleum products. Some alleviation of this burden has been obtained since 1955 through the installation of large diameter pipeline and a more intensive use of water transport. Plans for 1965 call for a more rational distribution of petroleum freight among the various carriers, with pipelines to account for about 34 percent of total ton-kilometers (TKM) of oil freight in that year, compared with only 13.8 percent in 1958.

A. Petroleum Pipeline Construction

At no time during the postwar period has the USSR been able to fulfill an annual plan for the construction of petroleum pipeline. The goal for construction of petroleum pipeline during the Fifth Five Year Plan (1951-55) was fulfilled by only 80 percent, and of the 6,525 kilometers planned for 1956-58, only 3,970 kilometers were actually installed for use, as shown in Fig. 13.

Petroleum pipeline construction during the five-year period 1956-60 totalled 7,785 kilometers. The Sixth Five Year Plan (1956-60), which originally covered these years but which was later superceded by the Seven Year Plan, had forecast the construction of 14,500 kilometers of petroleum pipeline and 9,000 kilometers of gas pipeline. Subsequently and in order to take full advantage of the economies of expansion of the production of natural gas, these goals were revised and the emphasis shifted to natural gas pipeline construction. Under this shift, the goal for construction of petroleum pipeline was reduced to 10,500 kilometers and that for gas was increased to about 16,000 kilometers. Yet the actual construction of petroleum pipeline during 1956-60 falls considerably short of meeting even this reduced goal.

The original Theses of the Seven Year Plan, published in 1958, state that 28,600 km of petroleum pipeline were to be installed during 1959-65. Later reports from authoritative Soviet sources implied that a more realistic goal of 21,000 kilometers of pipeline, including 13,500 kilometers of crude lines and 7,500 kilometers of product lines, applied to this period. It is possible that the goal of 21,000 kilometers did not include construction of a pipeline from Irkutsk to Nakhodka and a pipeline from Tuymazy in the Urals-Volga oilfields to Leningrad. Construction of these two pipelines may have been considered to be dependent entirely upon the procurement of steel line pipe from Western sources and therefore may have been excluded from the firm commitments for 1959-65.

Most of the difficulty encountered by the USSR in meeting annual goals for construction of petroleum pipeline may be attributed to the lack of large diameter steel pipe and indirectly to the desire to expand the natural gas distribution system. During the past several years, the domestic demand for steel pipe has exceeded the domestic capacity for production

Table 42

Construction of Oil Pipelines in the USSR
1896-1945

Origin	Intermediate Points	Terminus	Service	Length (km)	Dia. (in.)	No. of Pumping Stations	Date of Completion
Baku (after 1931, converted to crude)		Batumi	Product	883	8	16	1896-1906
Groznyy (after 1933, converted to crude, with flow in the reverse direction)		Makhachkala	Product	162	8	4	1910-1913
Tukha		Krasnodar	Crude	102	8	na	1910-1911
Dossor (later converted to the transport of water. No longer in use)	Rakusha	Kaspiy	Crude	154	6	na	na
Groznyy		Tuapse	Crude	649	10	7	1926-1928
Baku (Dismantled during WWII and rebuilt as a product line Astrakhan'-Saratov, length 650 km, 8 pumping stations, completed in 1943		Batumi	Crude	834	10	13	1927-1930
Armavir (In 1932, connected at Konokovo to the crude line Groznyy-Tuapse, thus forming the 879 km product line Groznyy-Konokovo-Armavir-Nikitovka, with 6 pumping stations)		Nikitovka	Product	455	12	2	1931
Ishimbay (Now a product line)		Ufa	Crude	168	12	na	1936
Guy'yev		Orsk	Crude	710	12	7	1934
Koschagyl		Pumping Station No. 3 the Gur'yev-Orsk line	Crude	120	10	1	1934
Malgobek		Groznyy	Crude	120	10	1	1940
Okha (Later extended to Komsomolsk, forming a 618 km line, with 3 pumping stations)		Sofiyskoye	Crude	390	12	na	1942
Zol'niy (Later paralleled along the Yablonovyy-Syzran' section)		Syzran'	Crude	136	12	na	1941

Table 43

Construction of Oil Pipelines in the USSR*
1946-58

Origin	Intermediate Points	Terminus	Service	Length (km)	Dia. (in.)	No. of Pumping Stations	Date of Completion
Tuymazy		Ufa	Crude	156	14	2	1947
No. 2			Crude	156	12		1953
No. 3			Crude	156	na	1	1954
No. 4			Crude	156	20	2	(1955?)
No. 5			Crude	156	28	1	1957
Ufa (continuation of Tuymazy–Ufa No. 4)		Omsk	Crude	1,183	20	7	1955
Ufa (continuation of Tuymazy–Ufa No. 5)	Omsk	Tatarskaya	Crude	800	20	6	1958
Ufa		Omsk	Gasoline	1,183	12	11	1955
Ufa		Petropavlovsk	Products	1,107	20	3	1958
Omsk		Novosibirsk	Products	691	20	5	1958
Bavly		Kuybyshev	Crude	314	na		1950
No. 2			Crude	314	na	3	1953
Shkapovo		Ishimbay	Crude	146	20	1	1956
Kaltasy	Chekmagush	Ufa	Crude	280	12	2	1958
Kuybyshev		Syzran'	Products	125	20	1	1955
Kuybyshev		Saratov	Crude	356	12	2	1955
Romashkino		Voskresensk	Crude	250	na	1	1954
Al'met'yevsk		Gor'kiy	Crude	577	12	5	1958
Al'met'yevsk		Subkhankulovo	Crude	105	20	1	1956
Al'met'yevsk	Karabash	Klyavlino	Crude	100	15	2	1953
Al'met'yevsk		Perm'	Crude	446	20	2	1957
Zhirnoye		Stalingrad	Crude	310	12	2	1957
Izberbash		Makhachkala	Crude	60	na	1	1952
Vyshka		Krasnovodsk	Crude	180	8	1	1949
No. 2			Crude	180	na		1954
Ozek Suat		Groznyy	Crude	200	12	4	1955
Voy-Vozh		Ukhta	Crude	110	na	1	1947

* With the exception of the Izberbash-Makhachkala line, only those lines with lengths of 100 km
and above are included in this tabulation.

Table 44

Transport of Petroleum Freight in the USSR by Type of Carrier
1940, 1950, 1955, 1958 and 1965 Plan

Year	Type of Carrier	Million Metric Tons Originated	Billion Ton-Kilometers	
			Amount	Percent of Total
1940	Rail	29.5	36.4	54.6
	Maritime	19.6	14.4	21.6
	Inland waterway	9.7	12.1	18.1
	Pipeline	7.9	3.8	5.7
	Total	66.7	66.7	100.0
1950	Rail	43.2	52.0	64.4
	Maritime	15.8	11.9	14.7
	Inland Waterway	11.9	12.0	14.9
	Pipeline	15.3	4.9	6.1
	Total	86.2	80.8	100.0
1955	Rail	77.6	101.6	65.8
	Maritime	23.0	23.9	15.5
	Inland waterwat	14.4	14.3	9.3
	Pipeline	51.7	14.7	9.5
	Total	166.7	154.4	100.0
1958	Rail	112.5	154.0	62.7
	Maritime	30.2	42.0	17.1
	Inland Waterway	16.2	15.8	6.4
	Pipeline	94.9	33.8	13.8
	Total	253.8	245.6	100.0
1965 Plan	Rail*	210	251	46.1
	Maritime	50	85	15.6
	Inland Waterway	24	24	4.4
	Pipeline	170	185	33.9
	Total	454	545	100.0

*Recent information indicates that the original goals for rail transport of petroleum have been revised upward. For 1965, the tons-originated reportedly has been increased from 210 million tons to 230 million tons and ton-kilometers from 251 billion to 270 billion. It is likely that these revisions reflect probable increases in petroleum traffic resulting from anticipated above-plan production, rather than a re-apportionment of the original 1965 goal for movement of oil freight.

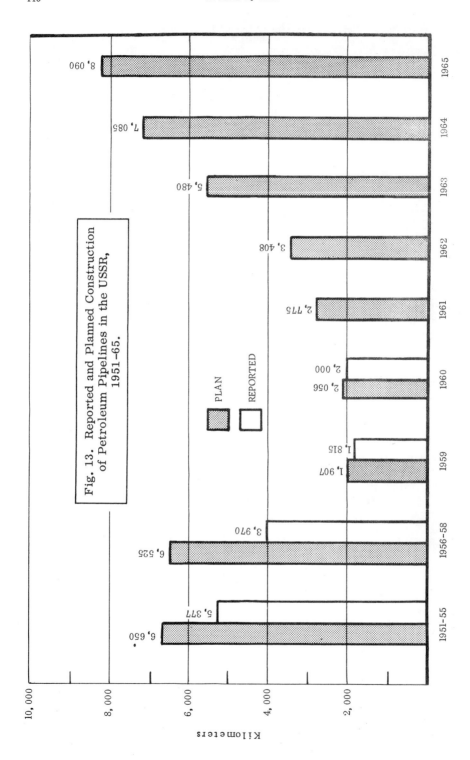

Fig. 13. Reported and Planned Construction of Petroleum Pipelines in the USSR, 1951–65.

by about 25 percent to 30 percent, and imports from Western sources have not been sufficient to cover this deficit. Most of the imports of steel pipe have been used in the construction of natural gas pipelines. These imports have been sufficient to allow the fulfillment of annual goals for construction of natural gas pipelines, although deliveries of steel pipe from domestic sources to the gas industry have been declining. Early in 1961 the chief of the Main Administration for the Gas Industry (Glavgaz) complained that pipe deliveries from domestic sources for natural gas pipeline in 1960 were only 94 percent of the 1959 level and were to be reduced in 1961 to 80 percent of 1959 deliveries. Thus, despite the apparent high priority attached to the development of the gas industry in that valuable foreign exchange had been utilized in an attempt to cover the deficit in large-diameter steel pipe, the priority was being shifted, temporarily at least. A major portion of imported pipe for the gas industry was 40 in. diameter pipe from West Germany. These imports were sufficient to allow construction of a gas pipeline system 40 in. in diameter and about 1,200 kilometers in length.

Table 45

Natural Gas Pipeline Availability in the USSR
1940, 1950, 1955-60, and 1961 and 1965 Plans

Year	End-of-Year Availability (Kilometers)	Annual Construction (Kilometers)
1940	139	–
1950	2,865	–
1955	5,889	–
1956	7,920	2,031
1957	10,120	2,200
1958	13,239	3,119
1959	17,092	3,853
1960	21,538	4,446
1961 Plan	25,266	3,728
1965 Plan	39,239	–

Because the Soviet oil pipeline program has failed to meet any of the annual goals since 1955, despite the growing emphasis on expanding oil exports, a re-examination of the relative priorities of oil and gas pipeline construction apparently has been made. The effects of this re-examination are evident in the 1961 goals for pipeline construction. Whereas the goal for construction of gas pipeline has been reduced by about 16 percent, compared with construction in 1960, a 40 percent increase in the annual construction of oil pipeline has been planned.

At the same time, the USSR announced its intent to construct almost 27,000 kilometers of oil pipeline during the years 1961-65. Annual construction plans for this period, in addition to pipeline availability in earlier years, are shown in Table 46. This apparent upward revision in the goal for construction, which if met would exceed the original Seven Year Plan requirements, may have been the result of successful negotiation with Western suppliers for significant imports of large-diameter pipe. Within the period of several months, the USSR announced purchases of 240,000 tons of pipe from Italy, 135,000 tons from Sweden, and 150,000 tons from England. The pipe from Italy and Sweden is to be 40 inches in diameter. In addition, negotiations are continuing with Japan which involve

Table 46

Petroleum Pipeline Availability in the USSR
Selected Years 1913-65

End of Year	Availability (Kilometers)
1913	1,147
1940	4,068
1950	5,444
1955	10,491*
1956	11,600
1957	13,187
1958	14,461
1959	16,276
1960	18,276
1961 Plan	21,051
1962 Plan	24,459
1963 Plan	29,939
1964 Plan	37,024
1965 Plan	45,114

*Including an estimated 7,400 km of crude lines and an estimated 3,100 km of product lines.

a possible delivery of 640,000 tons of steel pipe. All of the agreements already completed extend through 1965.

Table 47 lists those major oil pipelines scheduled for construction during 1959-65. Those oil pipelines of the USSR in use, under construction and planned are shown on Map No. 5.

It is estimated that about 9 million tons of steel pipe will be needed during 1959-65 to meet the goals for construction of trunk oil and transmission gas pipelines. An additional 4 million tons of steel will be needed for the construction of gathering lines and city gas distribution systems.

Of the total of 31,000 to 32,000 kilometers of oil pipeline which may be installed during 1959-65, about 18,000 kilometers are to be crude lines and the remaining 13,000 kilometers product lines. Emphasis has been placed on the construction of crude oil pipelines to ensure that by 1965 all of the crude delivered to refineries will be carried by pipeline. Trunk crude lines carried more than 80 percent of crude production in 1959, but only 20 percent of the output of light products were transported by pipeline. The need for a major expansion of the product pipeline network is considerably reduced as a result of Soviet practice of locating new refineries

Table 47

Major Oil Pipeline Construction in the USSR, Planned for 1959-65

Origin	Terminus	Length (km)	Probable Diameter (in.)	Service
Omsk	Irkutsk	2,470	28	Crude
Omsk	Chita	3,500	20	Products
Irkutsk	Nakhodka*	3,500	28	Crude
Tuymazy	Leningrad	1,500	28**	Crude
Kuybyshev	Mozyr'	1,350	40	Crude
Mozyr'	Brest	475	24	Crude
Mozyr'	Uzhgorod	725	24	Crude
Unecha	Polotsk	375	28	Crude
Polotsk	Klaipeda	475	24	Crude
Polotsk	Ventspils	475	24	Products
Kuybyshev	Bryansk	1,184	28	Products
Stalingrad	Tuapse	700	28	Crude
Ishimbay	Orsk	334	28	Crude
Petropavlovsk	Atbasar	720	20	Products
Omsk	Pavlodar	420	28	Crude
Gor'kiy	Ryazan'	415	28	Crude
Michurinsk	Kremenchug	700	24	Crude
Ozek Suat	Groznyy	194	15	Crude
Ryazan'	Moscow	250	20	Products
Ryazan'	Moscow	250	20	Crude
Al'met'yevsk	Gor'kiy	580	28	Crude
Kaltasy	Ishimbay	323	20	Crude
Stalingrad	Kuypansk	500	na	Products
Groznyy	Chaplino	1,100	na	Products
Shungay	Saratov	275	na	Crude
Shungay	Stalingrad	250	na	Crude

* Construction dependent upon obtaining pipe from Japan.

** Some use of 40" pipe may be made on this line.

near the centers of consumption and not necessarily near the source of crude oil.

Annual shortfalls in the plans for installation of pumping stations on new lines and on those lines already in use also serve to reduce the effectiveness of the Soviet pipeline network. In 1956, only 25 percent of the planned number of stations were placed into service; in 1957, only 50 percent of the planned number; and in 1958, not a single station was placed in use. A Soviet authority has pointed out that the volume of movement of by pipeline could be increased by as much as 10 billion to 15 billion TKM merely by building and putting into operation the planned pumping stations.

The lag in installation of pumping stations has precluded the achievement of the annual goals for transport of petroleum by pipeline. Concomitant with the reduction in planned construction of petroleum pipeline during 1956-60, as described above, the planned volume of POL movement by pipeline for 1960 was also reduced, from 83 billion TKM to 64-65 billion TKM.

Actual performance in 1960 was about 51 billion TKM. The goal for 1965 has been reported to be about 185 billion TKM. Fulfillment of the construction goal, the use of larger diameter pipe, and the installation of adequate pumping capacity may guarantee the achievement of this goal.

Despite a lack of steel pipe, inadequate pumping equipment and low utilization of existing capacity, pipelines provide the cheapest form of transport of POL in the USSR. The cost of transport of crude oil and petroleum products in 1959 averages as follows:

> trunk pipeline :   1.18 kopecks per ton-kilometer
> railroad   :   3.26 kopecks per ton-kilometer
> water   :   1.6 to 1.7 kopecks per ton-kilometer

The total cost of movement of oil freight by all means in 1959 reached nearly 6.4 billion rubles ($ US 1.6 billion), with nearly 83 percent of the total allocated to railroads. Expenditures for pipeline transport reached 540 million rubles ($ US 135 million) and represented less than 9 percent of the total.

B. Major Oil Pipeline Systems Planned, 1959-65

1. USSR-Satellite oil pipeline

One of the most highly publicized construction projects of the USSR in recent times and one which will serve to bind the European Satellite nations even closer with the Soviet Union is the so-called "pipeline of friendship." This pipeline, about 4,500 kilometers in length, is designed to supply the countries of Poland, East Germany, Hungary, and Czechoslovakia with crude oil for their expanding refining industries. Branch pipelines in the USSR will draw off some quantities of crude oil from this pipeline for delivery to refineries planned or under construction at Polotsk, Mozyr' and Kremenchug. But of particular importance to western nations is the Soviet intent to link this pipeline system with the Baltic Sea port of Klaipeda and probably also with the port of Ventspils. It is probable that completion of this link will permit an intensive drive for oil markets in Scandinavia and Northern Europe.

The Soviet Union began construction on that portion of the pipeline which lies within Soviet boundaries in early 1961. During this year, work is to be concentrated on the head of the pipeline, at Al'met'yevsk in the Urals Volga and west toward Kuybyshev, and on a 325-kilometer section from Brody to Uzhgorod, both in the Ukraine.

From Kuybyshev the pipeline is to extend westward to Unecha, where a branch line will be constructed to Polotsk and purportedly to Klaipeda, although recent statements by the chief of pipeline construction in the USSR have indicated that Ventspils will be tied in and that this port will be the major exporting base. Enroute to Unecha, a branch line is to be constructed from Michurinsk through Liski to a planned refinery at Kremenchug. It is possible that a products line may be built from Kremenchug to Odessa on the Black Sea, thus increasing Soviet export capacility from this area. The trunk line will continue on from Unecha to Mozyr', in Belorussia, where it will split into a northern section and a southern section. The northern section will extend from Mozyr' westward to Brest, on the Soviet-Polish border, then on to supply a refinery under construction at Plock (Poland) and another at Schwedt (East Germany), as shown on Map no. 6. Capacities of the Plock and Schwedt refineries have been reported at 2 million tons each.

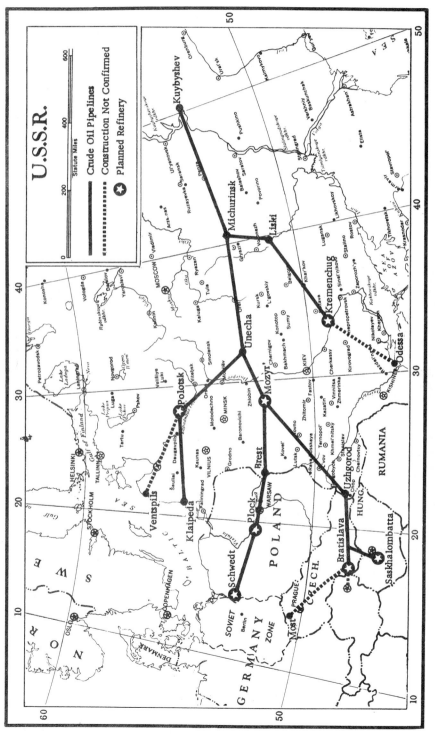

Map No. 6. The USSR–European Satellite Crude Oil Pipeline System

The southern section will extend from Mozyr' to Uzhgrod, in the Ukraine, where it will enter Czechoslovakia and continue to Bratislava, to supply a new refinery at this site. A branch line is to be completed off the Czech segment to Saskhalombatta, Hungary, also to provide charge for a new refinery. Capacities for these refineries are not known. Installation of sections from Bratislava to Most' and to Vienna are subject to speculation, but cannot be confirmed.

The Czechoslovakian segment and the Polish segment reportedly will be completed for use in 1962. Installation of the Soviet portion of the system may not be finished until 1964, and until that time the completed sections of the system will be filled with crude carried by rail tank car.

The major portion of the system, the 1,300 kilometer Kuybyshev-Mozyr' sector, reportedly is to be constructed of 40-inch diameter steel pipe, which would mark the first use of such diameter pipe in the construction of a trunk crude line. The USSR claims that use of 40-inch pipe will allow the movement of 5,000 tons of petroleum per hour. Diameters of the pipeline within Poland and Czechoslovakia fall within the range of 20-24 inches.

2. The Trans-Siberian Pipeline System

Completion is anticipated in 1962 of the Trans-Siberian crude oil pipeline which will link the new oil refinery at Irkutsk in Eastern Siberia with the oilfields of the Urals-Volga. This pipeline, 28 inches in diameter, has a total length of 3,700 kilometers. Plans do not call for an extension of this pipeline beyond Irkutsk during the remaining years of the Seven Year Plan, but negotiations have been underway for some time between the USSR and Japan which envisage continuation of the pipeline beyond Irkutsk to the port of Nakhodka, east of Vladivostok. These negotiations anticipate a large sale of crude oil to Japan, payment for which would be made in the form of steel pipe to be used in the construction of the pipeline. In addition, Japan would supply rail tank cars for the transport of the crude oil until the line was completed.

Paralleling the Trans-Siberian crude oil pipeline is a products line now under construction and planned for completion to Chita by 1965. Available information does not indicate an intent to lay branch lines into Communist China either from the crude line or the products line.

3. The Leningrad Oil Pipeline

Another major pipeline, the construction of which probably would have an impact on Western markets, is a crude oil pipeline designed to link the Urals-Volga oilfields directly with Leningrad. It is possible that 40-inch pipe may be used on a major sector of this line, apparently scheduled for completion during 1962-65. This pipeline probably will be used to supply crude oil to expanding refinery capacity in Gor'kiy, Ryazan', and Yaroslavl'. There has been some indication, although as yet unsubstantiated,

---

*This section will parallel a products line, extending from Kuybyshev to Bryansk, which has been under construction for the past several years. This products line is often misrepresented in the western press as that oil pipeline which is to be built to Klaipeda.

that a new refinery may be constructed at Kirishi, located about 120 kilometers southeast of Leningrad. It is probable that the pipeline would be able to carry sufficient quantities of crude oil beyond those needed by these refineries and thus to allow the export of substantial volumes from Leningrad.

XIV. STORAGE

As a part of the reorganization of the system of central marketing organizations, the marketing bases and warehouses were transferred to the jurisdiction of an appropriate republic sovnarkhoz or to the appropriate glavneftesbyt, attached to the gosplans of the constituent republics.

It is estimated that the total storage capacity for crude oil and petroleum products in the USSR at the beginning of the Seven Year Plan reached about 40 million tons. Of this quantity, crude oil storage capacity accounted for a probable 40 percent, and petroleum products - 60 percent. This capacity reportedly is to double during the period 1959-65. Thus total storage capacity at the end of 1965 may be estimated at 80 million tons.

Included in the total storage capacity is both primary storage and secondary storage. Glavneftesbyt controls only the primary storage bases, that is, those bases which handle the movement of crude oil from the field to the refinery and of petroleum products from refineries to the local distribution points. Glavneftesbyt does not control the secondary storage bases which are those at the consumer level.

Glavneftesbyt in 1955 controlled a total of 1,746 storage bases, the distribution of which by Economic Region* of the USSR is shown in the following:

Region	Number of Bases	Region	Number of Bases
I	81	VII	354
II	102	VIII	111
III	304	IX	132
IV	135	X	184
V	69	XI	69
VI	168	XII	37

As expected, the distribution of these bases among the various regions of the country reflects to a great degree the regional demand for petroleum products. To handle the increasing flow of crude oil and petroleum products within the USSR, additions to the number of POL storage bases have been necessary. It is estimated that this number reached 1,820 in 1960. The program of broadening the capacity of the storage bases has involved the expansion of capacity at bases in use, the construction of new bases, and the relocation of others from areas where the need for petroleum products has been offset by the use of other fuels.

Of the total of 1,746 storage bases, more than 94 percent were classified as distribution bases and the remainder, less than 6 percent, as transfer bases. The distribution base is the chief link between the petroleum industry

---

*See Map No. 3, USSR Petroleum Resources, 1958 for geographical definition of the various economic regions.

and the national economy. Petroleum products are delivered to these bases by rail, water, pipeline or by truck, and then are distributed to the consumer by small barge, tank truck, and in small containers. Storage capacity at the distribution bases is much smaller than that of transfer bases. In addition, a smaller number of petroleum products is handled. Certain products, such as aviation fuel, furnace oil and bunker sea mazut, are delivered directly to the consumer and bypass the distribution base.

The transfer base is located at sea ports, on the banks of navigable rivers, and in the areas of large railroad junctions. At these points crude oil and petroleum products are discharged from ocean-going tankers and from barges and are transferred to rail tank cars. In some cases, the procedure may be reversed. At certain transfer bases, crude oil and petroleum products are transferred from road-stead barges to river barges or to rail tank cars. At others, crude oil from the field or petroleum products from a refinery are delivered to the base by pipeline and then loaded into tank cars or into petroleum vessels. Storage capacity at the transfer bases usually is quite large, and the period of storage generally quite short.

Means of Storage

Cylindrical steel tanks provide the usual means of storage of crude oil and petroleum products in the USSR. Much publicity has been given to the use of prefabricated steel storage tanks which, according to Soviet engineers, allows a significant reduction in costs and in length of time of installation, compared with the usual means of installation. Under this new method, the steel plates are welded together at the factory, forming a roll which is delivered to the field. In the field, this roll is unwound and the completion of the wall requires only a single vertical weld*.

Until recently, the USSR claimed that this method was applied to most of the storage tanks under construction. But apparently the shortage of steel has forced the reduction in use of such methods and the petroleum industry currently is turning to the use of reinforced concrete storage facilities. Experiments also have been reported on the utilization of washed-out salt strata for the underground storage of petroleum products. Preliminary tests have proved successful, particularly in the Bashkir ASSR, where such deposits of salt are available.

XV. SOVIET TRADE IN PETROLEUM, 1955-60
AND PROJECTIONS FOR 1965

A. 1955-60

Much has been written concerning the growing role of the Soviet Union as an exporter of crude oil and petroleum products. Total exports from the USSR have increased from 8 million tons in 1955, the first postwar year which marked the USSR as a net exporter, to an estimated 30 million tons in 1960. During the years 1955-60 approximately one-half of the Soviet exports of petroleum have been delivered to Free World markets.

The move into Free World petroleum markets has both political and economic overtones. For sales of petroleum to underdeveloped and politically uncommitted countries the Soviet Union has accepted payment in

---

*See page 34 for details on construction.

soft currencies or in commodities for which these countries have a limited market. Offers of credit and technical assistance to the underdeveloped countries also have served to create closer ties with the Soviet Union and, at the same time, to reduce their reliance on Western suppliers.

In the industrialized countries of Europe, the sale of Soviet crude and products has as its purpose the procurement of goods and equipment which are in short supply in the Soviet Union and the disruption of normal channels of western trade. To secure a position in the European market, the USSR has employed the time-honored concept of cutting prices in order to dislodge already-established suppliers. It may be that the USSR wishes to realize the maximum return from its oil exports, but first has found it necessary to undercut current prices as a means of entering a market. Once the market is "captive" the price pattern changes abruptly. The average prices of crude oil and petroleum products sold to the Free World in 1957 and 1959, for example, were extremely favorable, when compared with prices paid by the Satellite nations.

	Satellites	Free World
1957 Price (rubles per ton)		
Crude oil	95.9	75.8
Products	183.8	106.3
1959 Price (rubles per ton)		
Crude oil	88.1	55.1
Products	158.2	75.8

Future prices may nearly reflect those quoted by Western suppliers after the desired market positions have been secured.

The recently concluded trade agreement with Italy, which calls for the import by Italy of 12 million tons of petroleum in exchange for 240,000 tons of steel pipe and other equipment, purportedly involved the sale of crude to Italy as $US 1 per barrel, f.o.b. the Black Sea. Such an offering could not be matched, of course, by Western companies under existing operating conditions. In the Italian agreement, and in other agreements entered into by the USSR, it is most difficult to construct any meaningful cost-price pattern. Such agreements must be evaluated on an individual basis. It is probable that the price of the crude oil to Italy was of secondary concern — in return for a surplus commodity, crude oil, the USSR is to receive significant quantities of steel pipe, a short supply item, needed for the expansion of its pipeline system.

The internal pipeline system may be fully capable of supporting the delivery of as much as 45 million tons, the equivalent of 900,000 barrels per day, of petroleum to Europe by 1965, if current construction plans are fulfilled. By that time, the domestic production of certain commodities, now in short supply and for which petroleum is being bartered, may have been brought up to the level needed to meet requirements. Based on present estimates of Soviet needs for all types of Western capital equipment, it appears unlikely that this independence will occur within the next five years, that is, also not earlier than 1965.

Once the USSR has established itself in the European markets as the flow of Soviet oil increases but the demand for Western equipment declines, the motivation in this area may shift to political. At this point, then, the USSR may begin to use its sales of petroleum to Europe for political, rather than economic, gains.

Because of the government control of the oil industry, the movement of petroleum out of the USSR may be manipulated to the very best advantage. A high degree of flexibility in selecting the most advantageous moment or place of sale can be achieved. This flexibility is not always available to the Western suppliers. To gain a sale or penetrate a market, any variety of terms may be accepted. The petroleum may be bartered for coffee from Brazil or wool from Uruguay. The recognition and exercising of this flexibility has secured for the USSR political and economic gains which far outweigh the volumes of petroleum which it has placed into international trade.

Table 48

Exports of Petroleum from the USSR
1955-60 and 1965 Estimate

| Year | Total Exports of Petroleum From the USSR (Million Metric Tons) | To the Free World | |
		Amount (Million Metric Tons)	As Percent of Total
1955	8.0	3.3	41.2
1956	10.1	5.0	49.5
1957	13.7	6.1	44.5
1958	18.1	8.7	48.1
1959	25.4	14.6	57.5
1960	30	19	63.3
1965 Estimate	70	45	64.3

B. Projections for 1965

The total supply of liquid hydrocarbons in the USSR in 1965 is estimated at 273 million tons which includes, in addition to 265 million tons of crude oil, an estimated 6.0 million tons of natural gas liquids and 2.0 million tons of synthetic products.

Of the total supply, allocations to meet the requirements of the civil and military sectors of the economy in that year may account for 187.5 million tons. Reported trade agreements between the USSR and the European Satellite nations covering 1965 plus probable deliveries to Communist China may account for an additional 25 million tons. Thus, the residual exportable surplus available for sale to Western countries in 1965 is estimated at 45 million tons of crude and products or 900,000 b/d, as illustrated in Table 50 and in Fig. 14.

Assuming that such a quantity would be available for export to Western countries questions the Soviet capability to move this volume to tidewater. Certainly the already over-taxed railroad system would not be able to take on any substantial, additional burden. Waterways are competitively economic but are subject to seasonal limitations. In essence, the level of success achieved in the construction of new trunk oil pipeline during the remaining years of the Seven Year Plan may well mirror the Soviet capability to export petroleum in 1965. To secure this success, the Soviet

Table 49

Imports of Petroleum into the USSR
1955-60 and 1965 Estimate

Year	Total Imports (Million Metric Tons)	From the Free World	
		Amount (Million Metric Tons)*	Percent of Total
1955	4.4	0.5	11.4
1956	5.3	1.4	26.4
1957	4.3	1.1	25.6
1958	4.3	1.0	23.3
1959	4.4	1.0	22.7
1960	4.0	1.0	25.0
1965 Estimate	0	0	–

* Imports of petroleum from the Free World have been limited to reparation deliveries of crude oil by Austria. Originally these deliveries were scheduled at one million tons per year through 1965, but in 1958 and in the succeeding years the USSR has returned to Austria 500,000 tons. Beginning in July, 1961 and continuing through July, 1964, Austria is to deliver only 500,000 tons each year. The reparation deliveries then will be cancelled as of July, 1964.

Table 50
Net Trade in Petroleum by the USSR
1955-60 and 1965 Estimate

Million Metric Tons

Year	Exports	Imports	Net
1955	8.0	4.4	3.6
1956	10.1	5.3	4.8
1957	13.7	4.3	9.4
1958	18.1	4.3	13.8
1959	25.4	4.4	21.0
1960	30.0	4.0	26.0
1965 Estimate	70.0	0	70.0

Union must in the very near future significantly expand its internal pipe-rolling capacity or conclude trade agreements with foreign suppliers which would produce the needed quantities of steel pipe. Similar measures must be taken to alleviate the apparent lack of equipment for pumping stations. It is apparent that continued reliance upon Western suppliers as a source for steel pipe, pumps, and valves may to a large extent provide the solution to the problem of pipe shortages in the USSR and thus allow a continuation of the export program.

Of the estimated surplus of 45 million tons of petroleum available for export from the USSR to the Free World in 1965, it is probable that 25 million tons could be delivered to Black Sea ports by pipeline, assuming that current plans for pipeline construction in that are are carried out.

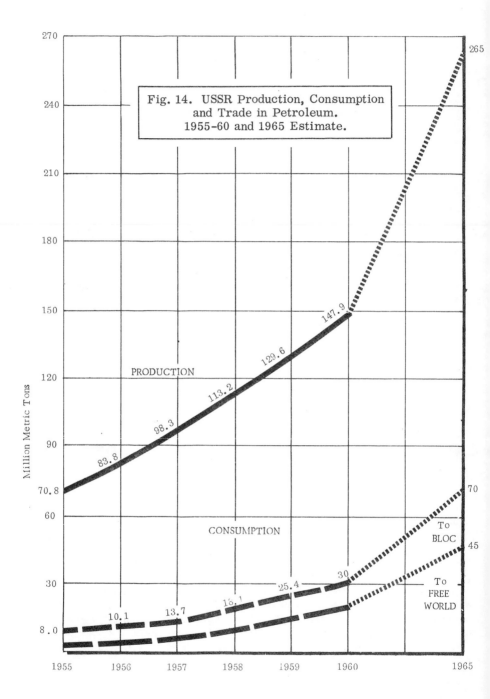

Fig. 14. USSR Production, Consumption
and Trade in Petroleum.
1955-60 and 1965 Estimate.

Table 51

Total USSR Exports as Percent of Crude Oil Production
1955-60 and 1965 Estimate

Year	Crude Oil Production (Million Metric Tons)	Total Exports (Million Metric Tons)	Exports as Percent of Production
1955	70.8	8.0	11.3
1956	83.8	10.1	12.1
1957	98.3	13.7	13.9
1958	113.2	18.1	16.0
1959	129.5	25.4	19.6
1960	148.0	30.0	20.3
1965 Estimate	265.0	70.0	26.4

Table 52

Estimated Supply and Demand for Petroleum in the USSR
1965

	Million Metric Tons
Supply	
Crude Oil	265.0
Natural Gas Liquids	6.0
Synthetics	2.0
Imports	0
Total	273.0
Demand	
Civil and Military	187.5
Losses, etc.	16.0
Exports to Bloc	25.0
Residual Exportable Surplus available for export to Free World	45.0
Total	273.0

Linking of the Urals-Volga oil fields by pipeline with the Baltic Sea ports of Klaipeda and Ventspils may portend the export of as much as 10 million tons from these ports in 1965. A similar amount may be available for export from Leningrad following completion of the Tuymazy-Leningrad crude line. It is probable that 10 million tons could be made available for export from the port of Nakhodka, should construction of a pipeline to that city from Irkutsk be undertaken.

Little difficulty is foreseen for the USSR in obtaining adequate tankerage for 1965. Barring any international emergency, the existing surplus of tanker capacity of some 10 percent probably will continue through 1965. An effective embargo on the chartering of Free World tankerage would force the

USSR to sharply expand its own fleet, if the export program were to be carried out. Based on current reporting, such as expansion apparently is being undertaken by the USSR. It is probable that utilizing its internal capacity and that of the East European nations, as well as purchasing of tankers abroad, the USSR will be able to float sufficient tankerage by 1965 to handle the exportable surplus.

The final question, then, addresses itself to the capability of the Free World but primarily of Western Europe, to absorb such large quantities of Soviet oil. Current estimates of the probable demand for petroleum products in 1965 show that a market will exist for Soviet oil. The USSR may encounter some difficulty in meeting world market quality standards, because of the lack of catalytic reforming facilities and because of the relatively high sulfur content of some of the Urals-Volga crudes. In addition, the low-octane content of the gasolines probably will preclude any significant export of this product.

APPENDIX A.

US Oil Delegation Notes on Meetings with Gosplan and Soyuznefteexport

MEETING WITH GOSPLAN — THE STATE PLANNING COMMISSION*

August 13, 1960 — Moscow
Kalamkarov   — Chief, Oil and Gas Section
Notkin, D.I.   — Chief, Oil and Gas Section,
                      State Scientific-Economic Council
Makhumdbekov   — Chief Engineer for Production
Shakhmatov   — Chief Specialist on Oil Production,
                      State Scientific-Economic Council
Sukhanov   — Assistant Chief, Oil and Gas Section
Krems   — Chief Technical Specialist,
                      State Schientific-Technical Committee
Basistov, Andros A.—Chief Specialist, Oil Refining,
                      State Scientific-Technical Committee

Members of both Gosplan and the State Scientific-Economic Council were present. These institutions are parallel in rank but Gosplan does the short range, the Economic Council the long range planning for virtually all Soviet industry. The Economic Council is working on a 20 year plan which it should have ready some time next year.

Our delegation stated its desire to ask a series of questions, admitting it did not expect all would be answered.

Question: The published goal for crude oil for the current Seven-Year Plan ending in 1965 is 240,000,000 metric tons per year. Is this still the goal?

Answer: Yes, this is correct even though the intermediate goals have been topped each year. The 1959 goal was exceeded by 1,800,000 tons although the 1960 half way mark is over by 2,000,000 tons, the goal for 1960 remains 144,000,000 metric tons. (A result of this is a continuing flow of bonus money to producing segments for exceeding quotas.)

Question: How are goals set by Gosplan?

Answer: Plans are made from the top down and from the bottom up. Some industries can do a satisfactory job on their own. Others, like petroleum, need help because outside demand is controlling. Plans are first worked up in the Economic Regions, then, go to the Gosplans of each Republic for reconciling production, consumption, and transportation. All these are handed to Gosplan and to the All-Union Economic Council for further review.

At this point, Mr. Notkin explained that the key to planning was balance and that Gosplan and the Economic Council had balancing departments whose function it was to equate all factors of supply and demand for the various industries.

---

*The reader may find that certain of the data presented in this interview either conflicts with or duplicates data in other sections of the report. The notes of this interview are presented primarily to illustrate the difficulties inherent in such a question—answer exchange with Soviet officials.

Regarding exploration, overall Soviet geological exploration is the business of the Department of Geology and Natural Resources which does most petroleum exploration. Nevertheless, Gosplan is responsible for some and, in places, goes ahead of the Department.

Question: Can you outline the current Seven-Year Plan product demand growth, especially with respect to: (a) motor car — fuel and lubes; (b) increasing role of oil in the USSR fuel balance; (c) increasing role of oil in the chemical industry. .

Answer: No definite answers. It was asserted that demand in all these lines was strongly up and that it was Gosplan's function to plan for the trends for both quality and quantity. This planning includes both internal and external commitments.

Question: Who determines what the refinery product quality will be?

Answer: The research groups advise Gosplan; Gosplan and the government decide whether to satisfy the product user or the refiner.

Question: Who innovates ventures?

Answer: Gosplan may direct a region to develop a needed industry. On the other hand a local economic council may counter with a better plan or may anticipate Gosplan by making the proposal first.

Question: What are the Seven Year Plans for petroleum transportation?

Answer: The goal is to have all crude move to the refinery and all products move from the refinery to large users by pipeline by the end of 1965. Products for small consumers will go by rail or water.

While total pipeline length will be modest the lines will be large diameter (1 meter average). A total of 32,000 kilometers of large diameter oil and product line will be laid within the current plan.

Question: What is the program for capital expenditures during the Seven Year Plan with respect to oil and gas?

Answer: Between 170 and 173 billion rubles. About 1/3 will go for exploration and development drilling (15% of drilling is said to be for structural exploration). Capital outlay for gas includes both pipelines and natural gasoline plants. Refinery outlay will include petrochemical units integrated with refinery construction. The figures do not include expenditures on nonproductive capital items as housing, transportation for employees, schools, hospitals, roads, etc.

Question: Is the rate of expenditure proceeding as planned?

Answer: Essentially so. In some cases completion is ahead of schedule and in general overall costs are less than anticipated. Expenditures in this seven year period will be 2-1/2 times the figure of the previous seven.

Question: How many people are employed in the petroleum industry and how is planning done with respect to training for future personnel needs?

Answer: As for other things plans for numbers and categories are made from the top down and the bottom up. To project demand for specialists is difficult. The Soviets simply observe the need for more and more, better and better trained men due to automation. In a sense availability of technical personnel dictates the rate of automation.

Medium grade technical training is handled locally in palaces of culture and high schools. Higher grade is done in regional institutes as at Baku, Ufa, Groznyy, Moscow, etc. A few years ago there were 500,000 employees in the petroleum industry including workers in related construction. There may now be 1,000,000. The oil industry is 2nd, 3rd, or 4th in the numbers of employees. A 35 to 40% growth is anticipated in the Seven Year Plan.

Question: How does the petroleum industry stand among others in wage rates?

Answer: In 3rd or 4th place. Rates for production workers, especially drillers, are higher than for refinery workers. The two highest paying industries are coal mining and open hearth steel operations.

Question: How are managements selected or developed for new enterprises?

Answer: This is the responsibility of the local economic council which in general tries to develop personnel within its region. Where specialists are not available it can reach out into other areas.

Question: How are product prices set (a) within the USSR? (b) for Communist Bloc countries? (c) for others?

Answer: Each enterprise calculates its cost of production, then establishes a wholesale price by adding 3 to 5 percent over cost. Most of the percentage remains with the enterprise; the rest goes to the State. Thus, an oil producing enterprise adds its percentage; the refinery adds its percentage; the transportation trust again, etc. The retained profit is used for technical plant improvements, housing, culture, etc. (Wage bonuses are considered part of the cost of production, i.e., do not come from the "profit.")

Other pricing factors are: (a) relative scarcity or abundance of the product; (b) the type of consumer. People vs. industry, for instances, or the type of industry; (c) the need for or value to the consumer.

Beyond this planned pricing done by Gosplan, additional price manipulation at the consumer level is done through the state levied, turnover tax. Gosplan has no hand in this. Within the Soviet Union prices vary according to zone. The number of zones will be cut and the arrangement will differ as against the July, 1955 report.

Pricing within the Soviet Union and the Bloc is used as a means of stimulating production and new industry. Prices for the Soviet Bloc and the outside world are set by trade agreements. Gosplan has nothing to do with this; it is the business of the Ministry of Foreign Trade. World price has to be considered but is not binding.

Question: What is the relationship between Gosplan and the Economic Council?

Answer: Formerly Gosplan did both long and short range planning. The impact of the increasing number of technical problems and technical advances on Gosplan made it advisable to create the Economic Council to deal with long range problems and plans.

Question: What agency is now in charge of research?

Answer: Petroleum research is a charge of the Economic Council although it is also locally done by individual enterprises so that it can be said that no one organization is in complete control of research.

Question: How does Gosplan coordinate petroleum with other industries?

Answer: Through interlocking Gosplan committees.

Other questions asked were sidestepped as adroitly as in the cases above.

General comments noted were that 1965 refinery runs were planned at 2.2 times 1958 runs and are, in fact, already 2.1 times that figure. USSR total charge figures were not given. Gasoline will remain at 20 percent of the total; diesel will go above 20 percent, fuel oils will increase.

There is an over supply of gasoline now which will be handled by directing manufacturers of diesel transport equipment to convert some models to gasoline.

Major export terminals will be on the Black Sea and at Klaipeda on the Baltic. A large pipeline is to be projected into eastern Europe beginning in 1961.

MEETING WITH SOYUZNEFTEEXPORT — THE ALL-UNION PETROLEUM EXPORT ORGANIZATION*

August 30, 1960 — Moscow

Present:
  USSR:
    E. Gourov, Director
    N.N. Zatchiniayev, Deputy Director
    U. Gorbunov, Interpreter
  US:
    George S. Dunham
    George Getty, II
    Noyes Smith, Jr.

The interview was conducted entirely in English, which Mr. Gourov speaks fluently. Although Mr. Gorbunov, our interpreter, was present, it was not necessary to use his services at any time.

Our first inquiries had to do with the function of Soyuznefteexport in the Soviet official hierarchy and its relationship to Gosplan.

Mr. Gourov explained that they were a government corporation which had the complete responsibility for trade in petroleum and petroleum products both for export and import. Under the Ministry of Foreign Trade there are some thirty specialized organizations handling different products as required by the Soviet economy, and theirs is the one which deals entirely with petroleum. It was explained that Gosplan would supply Soyuznefteexport with their estimate of materials for export and imports required. Soyuznefteexport, being the selling and purchasing branch, had the responsibility to review these proposed schedules, and if their estimate of the situation in the world market indicated that the proposed schedules were not feasible they could suggest alterations to Gosplan. These might or might not be accepted by Gosplan. If accepted, the new schedules became the operating plan. If there were differences between the two departments, the differences would be reconciled (as in other cases) by the Council of Ministers.

The next line of inquiry was directed toward the question as to whether the demands of bordering satellite countries were included in the USSR Seven Year Plan.

Mr. Gourov indicated that they were, and also that long-term commitments to countries in the Western world were also so included since they were a recognized demand on the Soviet oil industry. He pointed out that most of the satellite countries had long-term plans of their own, and that the pluses and minuses of petroleum demand in these local areas were picked up in the overall Soviet Seven Year Plan. It was stressed in Mr. Gourov's remarks that the deals with the bordering nations, as well as most of the commitments to Western nations, were under long-term trade agreements. We inquired what Soyuznefteexport considered long-term agreement, and it appeared that they felt that three to five-year deals

---

*From the notes of George S. Dunham.

could be so classified. It was stated that most of these agreements were couched in quite general terms, and that these general provisions were carried forward through the entire period of the deal, but that the details of the arrangements were worked out annually for the forward year.

The question was raised as to what mechanism the Soviet Union had found necessary to provide for price adjustment to reflect the changing world market prices.

Mr. Gourov explained that while prices could be renegotiated, it had not been found necessary to do so to any great extent. Most of these deals are made on a barter basis, in which there is the element of value of the goods to be acquired by the Soviet Union as well as the value of the oil which they export. He pointed out, for instance, in Poland, where oil was being exchanged for good-quality Polish coal, that although the world price for oil was low, at the same time the value of Polish coal was low in international commerce, and no adjustment had been found necessary. He also used a hypothetical illustration, where a Czechoslovakian manufacturer might have developed some new machinery which could be used in the Soviet Union. He pointed out that a three-year contract for the output of this plant in return for Soviet oil would be very advantageous to the machinery manufacturer since he would have an assured outlet for the production for a three-year period for a known and fixed price.

We asked for some information as to how such barter deals were established, since under the Ministry of Foreign Trade there were a large number of agencies dealing with the various products which the Soviet Union found necessary to buy from others. We directed this specifically to the current arrangement with Brazil.

Mr. Gourov indicated that such a barter arrangement could originate with Soyuznefteexport or with one of the other agencies in the Ministry of Foreign Trade. He pointed out that possibly Soyuznefteexport might see an opportunity to sell crude oil to Brazil, and that the Brazilian Government might suggest that coffee be purchased in return. The purchase of coffee would be referred to the agency dealing with "colonial products," which might be buying coffee in several areas of the Western world. If they agreed that it would be advantageous to concentrate their purchases in Brazil in exchange for Soviet crude, the deal would be worked out mutually under the general direction of the Ministry of Foreign Trade.

Since we had been discussing prices and barter arrangements, the next question was: How does Soyuznefteexport determine prices for deals with countries other than the satellites? Is there anything in the Soviet Union corresponding to posted prices which are generally used as references in Western nations' trading?

Mr. Gourov again commented that many of their deals with Western nations were on the bi-lateral trade-agreement basis, and that prices were therefore negotiated in view of the relative values of the commodities being exchanged. However, he stated that he kept currently acquainted with prices in the "Gulf," by which it was presumed he referred to the Persian Gulf. He stated, further, that they had given some consideration to establishing posted prices at the Black Sea and Baltic ports, and that they might do this some time in the future, although he made a strong point that posted prices were artificial and not representative of real values, and he saw no advantage to the establishment of another artificial basis by Soyuznefteexport.

We further inquired about the product pattern of Soviet exports which we might expect to find in the future, pointing out that we had been told that in their internal economy diesel oil demand dictated the amount of crude oil charged to refineries and that the refinery product pattern resulted in a long position in both gasoline and the heavy ends of the barrel.

Mr. Gourov said that this was indeed true; and that the Soviet Union would like to export large quantities of gasoline, but that the organization and facilities necessary to move gasoline into the Western world was much too expensive and that it would appear better for them to arrange to consume gasoline at home than to try to move it in the world market at a loss. They would therefore concentrate their efforts on materials which could be used in international trade without the necessity for investing in expensive facilities to move the product. He indicated these would be diesel oils, gas oil, fuel oil and lubricants. (Ninety percent of the Soviet product exports in 1959 to the Free World were diesel oils and fuel oil, in about equal volumes. This does not seem to confirm the statements the delegations had heard from others as to the difficulty of meeting internal diesel oil demand.) The products which they propose to sell can be sold in tanker lots and received in bulk storage owned by others.

At this point, he said, with a smile, that the Soviet Union had not seen fit to build tankers for deep-sea transportation in quantity, since the capitalist countries had done such an excellent job of over-building that the Soviet Union was in a very fine position to reap the benefits of the resulting low-cost transportation.

Mr. Gourov further stated that the Soyuznefteexport did not intend to destroy markets; that they were interested in getting full value for their crude and products, but that there were many places in the world where prices were unjustifiably high, and that they did not believe that such high prices and concurrently large profits were justified. In discussing their price policy, he pointed out, for example, that the Soviet Union was not shipping any goods to Switzerland, because the Swiss price structure was so low that the Swiss could not pay the price that the USSR was demanding for its oil.

Our next inquiry was directed toward crude oil. We inquired as to whether the function of Soyuznefteexport was to dispose of intermittent excesses of crude oil, or whether it was proposed to establish the Soviet Union as a crude-exporting nation.

Mr. Gourov replied that Soviet exports will not decrease. He stated that they had been expanding at the rate of 20 to 25 percent per year (our figures indicate closer to 40 to 45 percent), but since they had started from a very low base that such a rate would probably not continue into the future, although they might continue to increase from 15 to 20 percent per year. He then followed with the observation that there was a time when the Soviet Union was an important source of petroleum for the world, and he felt that they were just as much entitled to a share in the export business as any of the Western countries. He added that he realized there were areas in the world, such as South America, where Soviet oil could not compete economically. Trade with their non-Communist neighbors was, however, in the best interest of the Soviet Union, and he particularly stressed the Baltic countries as natural outlets for Soviet oil exports.

Japan was also mentioned as a "neighboring" country with which it is desirable to do business. Nothing was said about the economics of Soviet oil in this trade. The emphasis was entirely on Japan's industrial potential.

He stated that he did not object to competition for markets; he considered competition good and necessary; but he observed that some competitive methods which he had run up against he considered unfair. He felt that a more cooperative attitude by the international oil companies with the Soviet oil industry could be mutually beneficial. At this point we inquired, if the political atmosphere would change so that freer trade between our countries were possible, would Soyuznefteexport be interested in exchange agreements, such as crude oil on the Danube for crude on the Persian Gulf, or fuel oil at Baltic ports for fuel oil in the Caribbean. He replied with an enthusiastic "Yes," saying that any arrangements of this kind which would result in lower transportation cost would be highly desirable and they would certainly be open to such suggestions.

We inquired if the Soviet Union saw any threat to the Japanese market, which they had entered recently, coming out of Japanese production in the Persian Gulf.

He said he saw no problem there; he felt that the Japanese market will continue to grow at such a rate that there will be room for any production which Japan develops, without significantly reducing the demand from others, including the Soviet Union.

He has great hopes for the general increase of world demand, and sees many of the underdeveloped countries as an expanding market for petroleum. In this respect, we inquired about the Soviet plans with respect to Communist China. He disclaimed any intimate knowledge of the Chinese situation, and although the USSR is currently furnishing Communist China a large quantity of petroleum products they do not have any plans for extending a pipeline system into that country. A pipeline is being constructed to Irkutsk, which is on the border of Mongolia, but he informed us there were no plans to extend it either further east into Siberia or south into Communist China.

We commented on the apparent lack of storage facilities in the Soviet Union and asked how they were able to take care of short-term variations in supply and demand.

He fully agreed that their storage situation was inadequate, and stated that it was because the oil industry had expanded so rapidly in recent years they had been unable to build adequate storage as it was needed, but that tank farms were being constructed and they hoped to be in better position along this line in the future. At the present time it is necessary to control production and refinery runs closely in order to stay within the limits of their storage capacities.

The last question which we put to Mr. Gourov was about as follows: Soyuznefteexport, in common with all other segments of Soviet industry, must have some established goal under the Seven Year Plan. What would constitute over-fulfillment of that goal and qualify Soyuznefteexport for bonuses for achievement?

In spite of Mr. Gourov's excellent command of English, he found a great deal of difficulty in understanding the question, and no satisfactory answer was obtained.